STONED FREE
How To Get High
Without Drugs

STONED FREE
How To Get High
Without Drugs

by Patrick Wells
with
Douglas Rushkoff

Loompanics Unlimited
Port Townsend, Washington

This book is sold for information purposes only. Neither the author nor the publisher will be held accountable for the use or misuse of the information contained in this book.

Stoned Free: How To Get High Without Drugs
© 1995 by Patrick Wells and Douglas Rushkoff

Published by:
Loompanics Unlimited
PO Box 1197
Port Townsend, WA 98368

Loompanics Unlimited is a division of Loompanics Enterprises, Inc.

Cover design by Jim Woodring
Illustrations by Kevin Martin

ISBN 1-55950-126-X
Library of Congress Card Catalog 95-76191

Contents

Introduction

How many of you remember childhood afternoons spent spinning in circles in the backyard to see how dizzy you could make yourself? Or holding your breath for as long as you could, and even having a friend from down the block squeeze the air out of you from behind so you would almost pass out? Or taking your bicycle to the top of the steepest hill in town, and seeing if you could make it all the way down without hitting the brakes? Or were you the kind of kid who spent your recess listening and spacing out to the echoes and reverberations in a big metal sewer pipe?

These are all examples of self-induced alterations of consciousness: highs. Getting high is one of the most natural human urges. As Andrew Weil explained in *The Natural Mind*, "...the omnipresence of the phenomenon argues that we are dealing not with something socially or culturally based but rather with a biological characteristic of the species. Furthermore, the need for periods of nonordinary consciousness begins to be expressed at ages far too young for it to have much to do with social conditioning." While "highs" have gotten a bad reputation in the "just say no" decade, they need not necessarily be associated with drugs or psychedelics. In fact, non-chemical highs are almost invariably more enjoyable, longer lasting, and of greater benefit to one's quality of life.

2

The problem with drugs is manifold. First, most drugs are simply poisons. They alter your consciousness by fucking you up. Only one category of drugs, psychedelics (which includes marijuana, LSD, and mushrooms) produce what feels like an expanded state of consciousness, but these are limited and precarious experiences at best. Hallucinogens offer only a transitory look at a blissful state of mind. The user must invariably "come down," and without any of the skills necessary to integrate the ecstatic experience into daily life. Thus, there is little positive effect to the repeated use of these chemicals. Psychedelics are like window shopping; you get to see what it must be like to be enlightened, but are left wondering how to get there yourself.

The other main problem with chemically induced states is that it's hard not to associate the drug with the state of consciousness that follows its ingestion. In fact, it is not the drug which makes you high. The chemical only acts as a key to opening a state of consciousness which you already have available to you. The repeated use of drugs to unlock that door perpetuates the fiction that you couldn't get there by yourself. You can. This book will show you how.

Getting high on your own is like climbing a mountain instead of taking the chairlift. It's a little more difficult, and usually requires the development of one technique or another, but the results are always more grounded and more permanent. Instead of looking out on the mountain from a chair dangling from a wire that someone else erected, you stand on the face of the mountain on your own two feet. On drugs, you are not the master of your experience. Most psychedelic trips will last six to eight hours, and the quality of a given experience will be directly related to the quality of the chemical you have ingested. You have little or no control. (Some might argue that's the point of altering consciousness. Fine, but it doesn't have to be.) While it is possible to learn how to steer a trip, using Timothy Leary's variables of set and setting, (see Leary, Albert, Metzner, *The Psychedelic Experience*) you are still at the mercy of a chemical.

There are, however, many non-drug-related techniques available that result in a variety of different highs. In using any of these methods, it is important to bear in mind that the technique itself is not the high. If you learn, for example, to liberate your consciousness from the time-space continuum by spinning in Sufi dervish dances, you accept and appreciate the dance as a wonderful vehicle — not as an end in itself. Whatever technique you choose, remember that it is merely opening up a channel to your innate ability to expand your consciousness. The method has no power in itself.

You already know how to get high. You've simply allowed your mind to convince you that you forgot. At one time, you were an open channel, receiving signals from everything around you: lights, voices, textures, even thoughts and emotions bombarded you from everywhere. Devoid of judgment, you simply experienced everything, and filtered nothing. This was a state of complete awareness, if not complete comprehension. You had no ability or need to concentrate. All senses were alive at once. Growing up, however, you needed to develop the ability to select what you wanted to pay attention to and what you didn't. The mind you developed and carry with you now functions as a filter, enabling you to select certain stimuli, and avoid others. This is what allows you to read this book while ignoring people that may be walking around near you, or traffic noise from outside. If you shifted your awareness from the print on this page to the sounds outside, you could completely alter your state of consciousness without even moving a muscle.

So the mind acts like a gatekeeper of awareness, limiting what receives your attention. Employed as your consciousness' receptionist, the mind decides which calls get through and which don't. Most of us, however, have been letting our receptionists make too many of our decisions for us. The receptionist decides who is worth talking to and who isn't. The receptionist decides what we're conscious of and what we're not. Meanwhile, we have become prisoners behind our desks, no longer the boss of our office, but the servant of our employee. To us, reality is whatever our receptionist chooses for us. Don't misunderstand: the mind is not an evil gatekeeper. It has our best interests at heart; it just gets a little overprotective. The result is that we live in a limited reality.

Getting high is merely moving past the outer office into full-fledged reality. The mind no longer selects and edits what we per-

4

ceive. Instead, we return to the nonjudgmental awareness we had as babies. We no longer rely on our experience or memories to provide appropriate behavior for given circumstances, but instead we respond to every new event as if it were happening for the first time. We are in the moment. We are alive.

The methods for getting past the receptionist vary, but usually involve putting it to sleep, getting it extremely busy, or zoning it out. Often we experience a high during catastrophes. The mind is so busy dealing with danger or disaster that our consciousness is left temporarily unguarded. The next time you hear someone relating a car accident or other life-or-death event, notice how the storyteller seems to fix on strange details — the expression on the driver's face, the tone of the policeman's voice, or even the color of the sky. Unaccustomed to unfiltered reality, the freed consciousness doesn't know where to look.

The exhilaration associated with such events often leads sick minds to seek them out. This is the daredevil mentality that motivates benign thrillseeking as well as violent crimes. The same urge that gets us on a rollercoaster leads a less stable individual to drive down city streets at 100 miles per hour. A large part of the attraction to drugs is that we know there is a level of danger in using them. These activities are not what this book is about. Highs do not have to be scary to be fun.

Safe highs allow us to unlock the doors of perception rather than crash through them. The method used is unimportant, as long as it works and it doesn't hurt anybody. We soon realize that highs are not mere vacations from reality. They are excursions *into* reality. Living high becomes a preferred state of being.

In the last chapter, "Staying High," we will explain how peak experiences can be integrated into the rest of your life, but there are a few points about getting high that are worthy of consideration before you get started. Sometimes, because altered states are so much fun, they can make the rest of life seem dull by comparison. For example, if you really enjoy skydiving, your mind will start to divide experience into two categories: fun/skydiving and not fun/not skydiving. This is a mentality to avoid whenever possible. Just as with drugs, it is easy to identify the technique with the state of mind. They are not the same. Any technique, however sacred, is only a vehicle to a place that is already available to you.

It is also easy to allow a given high to overshadow something much greater: truly expanding your consciousness. Highs are great, but they are only a first step in the journey toward full awareness. Peak experiences are rewards along the way, to let you know you are traveling in the right direction. If you are open to highs, let them happen, and let them go, you will continue moving towards greater and greater ecstasy. The moment you hold onto a high, try to recreate it, or spend all your conscious time thinking back on it, you are just as stuck as when you began.

Attachments are the opposite of bliss. They are what the mind uses to keep you working at your desk. Concerns like money, outward success, security or the opinions of others are what the mind clings to and uses to box you in. Don't attach to your highs in this way, or they won't liberate you anymore. You will go on an endless search for new and better highs without ever really feeling satisfied. Altered states of consciousness can teach us how to live in the moment — not some moment that has already passed, however beautiful it may have been.

With this, then, we embark. Try what you like, skip what doesn't appeal to you. Under no circumstances do anything in this book without consulting your doctor first. Have fun, laugh at life, but don't be stupid. If you're hypoglycemic, don't go on a fast, and if you have a heart condition, don't go skydiving. Things like that. Enough said.

Chapter One:
Seeing Is Believing:
Visual Highs

The relationship between eyes and highs is obvious. One of the first questions veteran users of psychedelics ask about a given drug is "how are the visuals?"

The way things look is often the way we judge whether or not we are in an altered state of consciousness. Things might look clearer, brighter, more three dimensional, or kinetic. Sometimes we even see things that aren't there. In any case, things often look different when we're high.

One way of getting high on visuals is to look at something that initiates the optic experience of being high. Even if you have not been high before, the brain reacts to the altered vision by producing an appropriate altered consciousness. Some of the techniques in this chapter are simply things to look at, and brief instructions on the best manner in which to view them. These objects or drawings serve to activate the mind like a mantra. Slowly, as you stare, the object will appear to alter. As your vision alters, your mind follows. Most of these techniques exploit the visual center of the brain by manipulating your processing circuitry.

The limbic neocortex is believed responsible for processing the light our eyes receive into images. It does this by manipulating a set of about twelve already existing "grids" into a visual language. One of the grids, for example, looks like a field of tiny diamond shapes. Most of the others have not yet been observed individually. Each of these grids could cover your entire field of vision. Any object one looks at is received as a pattern of light by the eyes, then translated into a combination of geometric grids by the brain. Depending upon what you're looking at, any number of these grids may be activated over any portion of your field of vision.

If you gain direct access to the geometric grids of the limbic neocortex, you enjoy control over a usually passive part of the mind. You are in a position to experience the language of the brain on its preconscious level. Even more fascinating though, is that you are no longer looking at physical reality. You are observing inner space. Many philosophies consider external reality an illusion. This inner space is the true underlying reality in which consciousness and spirit exist. Or maybe not, but at least it looks really cool.

The latter techniques in this chapter allow you to see things which aren't "really" there. In this way, you can expose the brain to visual stimuli that are unavailable in daily life. Concentration on these hitherto unexperienced stimuli brings the mind into new places, and the consciousness into new realities.

Have fun with these techniques and, most importantly, go slowly and gently. Never force your eyes — relax them. Your eyes are important to your functioning. Doing anything that causes them pain is probably damaging them, and you should stop if you feel any discomfort.

Mandalas

Mandalas are complex circular drawings which people look at while they meditate. They are all based on the idea that everything emanates from a center, and throughout nature there are an infinite number of examples of this principle. The petals of a flower emanate from a center. The eye emanates from its iris. A spider web emanates from a central circle. An atom emanates from a nucleus. A solar system emanates from a sun. The reward of mandala work is a deep intuitive confirmation that the universe emanates from a single source: the mind of God, or the center of life energy.

Carl Jung was fascinated by mandalas. He observed their occurrence in nearly every culture in the world, from the Navahoes to the Tibetans, or from the I Ching to Stonehenge, and saw the repetitive images as a confirmation of his theory of the collective unconscious. Thus, he surmised, the symbols of the mandala themselves emanate from the core of human consciousness.

The techniques of working with mandalas vary as widely as the mandalas themselves. The simplest would be to find a mandala that you like (for excellent examples, see *Mandala* by José and Miriam Arguelles, Shambhala: 1972) or use the one in this book. Or use anything that appeals to you personally — from your lover's eyes to a hubcap.

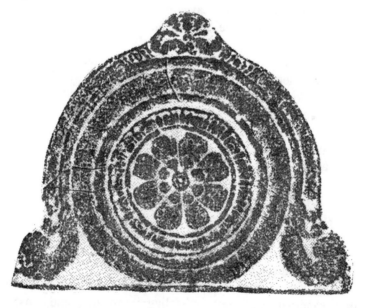

Relax your eyes, and look at the image. Gently force your attention on the center of the circle, but allow your awareness to include the entire mandala. If your consciousness drifts, gently bring it back to just looking at the mandala. After several minutes, you can allow your eyes to slowly move around the image, but be sure to avoid sharp, quick eye movements. After you feel you have taken the entire image in, close your eyes, and continue to "see" the mandala. You don't need to see it exactly as it looked. You might remember specific images or a generalized pattern. It is not important. After a few minutes of this, try to imagine this image as seen by an eye in the middle of your forehead — your third eye. You may need to open your eyes briefly to remember the mandala. Gently focus on your third eye "seeing" the mandala. Finally, allow your third eye to become the source of the mandala. It is not only seeing the image, but emanating it. Feel the radiance of the mandala move out through your body, into the space around you.

Constructing mandalas is usually even more satisfying than meditating on other people's. You can do this by painting, or by simply placing rocks, crystals or leaves in a circular pattern that pleases you. Children do this all the time. Then do the above steps on your own mandala.

Dhyana Mandala is a technique for creating and meditating on some of the archetypal mandala images. In his small workbook on the technique, (*Dhyana Mandala,* Shiksha Bharati: 1978) Brigadier Teg Bahadur Kapur shows how to construct many of these. You start by making a perfect hexagon out of any material (cloth, construction paper, even wood). The careful construction of the mandala is as important here as the later meditation. After doing the above meditation on the hexagon, which Kapur feels is the Master Symbol of life, you fold it into other, archetypal shapes.

While the images used here are not the circular, concentric mandala we are used to, they do emanate from the central image of the hexagon, as do all of the Dhyana mandalas.

The most intense experience of the mandala would be through a Native American shaman. These medicine men direct the creation of elaborate sand paintings used for healing, purification and consciousness expansion.

Monitor Highs

There are a number of videos and computer graphics programs out now that use a variety of methods to alter your consciousness.

The most effective either imitate the known geometric grids of the limbic neocortex, or work out complex mathematical equations in visual form. We tend to stay away from most of the New Age stuff out there, which usually involve photography of nature accompanied by soft music. We'd rather just go outside.

As for the former type, they're easy to use. Just shove a tape in the VCR or a floppy disk into the computer and go. We recommend turning the brightness control down on your television set, and turning off all the lights in the room. Most of these videos have soundtracks, but if you don't like their music try your own or watch in silence.

Our favorite tapes are computer generated, and based on fractal equations. They look great, and seem to resonate with something deep in your consciousness. In fact, fractals are simple math equations, like $y = 2x + 6$. For every input, x, there is an output, y. But instead of just graphing the resulting parabola for a fractal, each y value is plugged back into the equation, as a new x. Then that answer is plugged back into the equation and so on. The amazing thing about fractal equations is that they can explain nature. The pattern of growth of a fern, for example, can be entirely explained by about two fractal equations. More advanced ones can explain how cells differentiate in an embryo. In short, they are the mathematical representations of the process of life.

The equations would normally be graphed on a three-dimensional axis, but since a television or monitor is a two-dimensional screen, the depth of a given point is defined by its color. This results in wonderful landscapes of color, which are at once abstract and organic. They must be seen. The best fractal tapes are available through Fractal Vision, PO Box 1193, Aguora Hills, CA 91376 (818-889-5425). Ask for *Fractalidescope* by Arnie Greif, or *Fractal Fantasy* by Charlie Fitch.

Aeon Home Video has a new video on the market called *Fractal Lumination Volume 1*. It features a score by the Moody Blues, and a portion of the profits go to a reforestation charity. It's available by calling 800-ROCK ART.

Fractals, which are designed on a computer, can be viewed far better on a high-resolution computer monitor. A program called

12

Fractools was created to allow you to generate your own fractals or manipulate images from a library on disk. Effects available include "strobe," "kaleidoscope," "stained glass," and "mouse movies." You need an IBM computer, an EGA or VGA monitor, and a hard drive. For more information call Bourabaki, Inc., 800-289-1347.

The very best computer graphics programs, however, are made for the Macintosh. Todd Rundgren, musician cum computer hacker, has designed a stunningly beautiful screensaver program called *Flofazer*. Its official purpose is to protect your computer screen after you've left your system unattended; its true purpose is to dazzle you into altered states with swirling, colorful imagery. These pictures are *nice*. Rundgren has designed about thirty different patterns to choose from, and while a color monitor is not essential, it is 90 percent of the fun. These are the best visuals available anywhere. *Flofazer* is a masterpiece. Rundgren is a genius. Get the program directly from Todd at Utopia Grokware, 415-331-0714. An IBM version is also in the works.

Other kinds of mind-altering videos are created using optics, video feedback, and manipulation of raw images. These are sometimes billed as "guided meditations," like Shirley MacLaine's *Inner Workout*, but many are available with no talk. Ken Jenkins, the artist who created the effects for MacLaine's video, has several of his own works. The best is probably *Illuminations*. It's a very smooth-flowing study of light and color. Unlike the fractal videos, *Illuminations* is seamless, and allows you to float much longer. Most of the people who watch it have a Rorschach-type reaction and see angles or spaceships or parts of the body. It's available at most New Age bookstores or through Immediate Future Productions, PO Box 1341, Los Altos, CA 94023 (415-948-7834).

There are many videos to choose from. The following is a brief list of some we can recommend.

The Experiment at Petaluma is Terence McKenna's long-awaited venture in to psychedelic videography. It is billed as "an alchemical computer assemblage of thought, sound, and image" and is quite successful at re-creating stimulating visuals. Send $32.95 to ROSE X, Box 728, Petaluma, CA 94953.

California Images is a collection of twenty short pieces by California's top video artists. None are really long enough to take you in completely, but the video would be a good starting place if you are trying to find out what kinds of video works best for you. Contact Pilot Video, 425 Alabama Street, San Francisco, CA 94110 (415-863-3555).

Structures from Silence is a set of motion paintings by Marianne Dolan. Her description is probably best: "Join a dreamflight through liquid time when starfields shift, clouds implode and quivering plasma galaxies swell and are born." Contact the Ark Group, PO Box 410685, San Francisco, CA 94141-0685 (800-727-0009).

There are also several feature films on tape that produce vivid altered states of consciousness when viewed with that purpose. Take the phone off the hook, get a comfortable chair, clear your mind and relax deeply into the imagery on screen. Don't worry about plot and character. Just watch the images, the faces of characters, the movement of the camera and the changes of scenery.

We have found documentaries often work the best. You are watching real people behave, without having to be there. The perspective is novel. Try documentaries that aren't in English. Even animal or nature documentaries work as long as the filmmakers haven't imposed a story or strong sensibility of their own onto the images. Usually simple, repetitive tasks on film work the best — like a documentary on Indians building canoes, or the workings of a mannequin factory. Werner Herzog produced some excellent documentaries early in his career, but most are not available on videotape. Godfrey Reggio's *Koyaanisqatsi* and *Powaqqatsi* are both available on tape, and combine time-elapsed imagery, live-action footage and Philip Glass music.

Animated features like *Fantastic Planet* and *Light Years* have a science fiction emphasis, but also provide some stunningly simple visuals. Check your local video store for these and other weird films, and view them with the intention of melding with the imagery. Many people choose to watch these films when high, because they seem to conform with that state of consciousness. Fortunately, you can simply

14

relax your consciousness to conform with the film, and get very similar results without chemicals.

Also watch your local movie revival house's listings for a film called *The Valley* about a group of Europeans who go to an Indonesian island looking for exotic feathers. They find, instead, a very strange tribe, and end up getting involved in their rituals. Apparently, the group of actors making the film had a parallel experience as they shot the footage. The result is spectacularly mind-altering. The score is by Pink Floyd.

Sometimes the manner in which films are projected can affect you greatly. If you haven't been to an Imax theater, check that out. The screen is huge, and because of the way the seats are situated, you feel the illusion of motion. Go when they are showing a film about flying, and see how "into it" you can get. Try going with a group a similarly-minded friends, so you don't feel as strange falling into your own world as you watch.

Most planetariums now do laser shows on weekend evenings. Resist the temptation to get high before you go in; if you want, you can simply pretend you are high as you watch. Don't talk to anyone. Just breathe, relax and look up.

Strobes

If you are epileptic, or might be, don't do this. Pick up a strobe light at Radio Shack, a theater lighting store, or your neighborhood head shop. It should cost under fifty dollars. A strobe is a xenon tube which charges and discharges very quickly and completely. Unlike an incandescent bulb, which fades out when you turn it off, a xenon bulb does not ghost. It goes out immediately. For this reason, it is ideal for creating a strobe effect.

If you can't find or afford a strobe light, find the most directed and clear light you have. Some kind of spotlight would be ideal. It should be constructed in such a way that if you were to cover the opening with your hand, no light would escape. Put a large fan directly in front of the light, so that the flow of light is interrupted every time a blade of the fan swings by.

Go to a pitch black room (use a closet if you must) where you can sit down comfortably, three to eight feet away from your strobe light, which should be placed at eye level. Turn it on so it flashes at a rate of somewhere between ten and twenty flashes a second. If you're using a fan, put it on a slow speed. Stare directly at the bulb, leaving your eyes gently out of focus. If this is painful, try putting a blue gel filter in front of the bulb. As you sit and stare, you may notice a strange shape of light form between you and the light. Most people usually see it as a purplish glow, but it may look different to you. Concentrate on the apparition if one appears. Relax and wait.

Phosphene Stimulation

This is something most of us did as kids before we fell asleep at night, but has now become a lost art for us. It is an easy and effective way to reach extraordinary altered states of consciousness, and is practiced by shamans and monks alike. Some sects regard it as such a powerful technique that they disclose it only to trusted students. If you can be trusted, continue reading. (As with all the techniques in this book, ask your doctor first!)

Wash your hands and face well. Sit with your eyes closed, and gently press your closed lids with your fingers. Observe the colored or black spots that appear. Concentrate on these shapes as a meditation, or continue to manipulate with your fingers and watch them change. This can even be done with your eyes partly open, fingers pressing through the top or bottom lids, or from the sides. Try variations of this using ice, hot compresses, even a penlight.

Life In Soft Focus

The next time you are outside in a non-threatening environment (where there aren't cars to run over you, or cliffs to fall off) try this technique. There are shamans who say this is the only technique needed to reach complete enlightenment. While we can't attest to that, we can promise it will get you high.

16

Sitting or standing, very softly focus on a point ahead of you. Let your eyes relax so that the point you are looking at gets fuzzy. Without moving your eyes, shift your attention to your peripheral vision. Keep looking lightly ahead of you, while you place all of your awareness to your sides. If it helps, put your arms in front of you, and slowly spread them out to the edge of your field of vision. Wave your hands if you need to, but don't move your eyes to find them. Resist the temptation to focus your eyes for as long as possible.

After you get this down pretty well, try walking around, keeping your eyes in soft focus, and your attention on your periphery. According to Don Juan (Carlos Castaneda's teacher) this is "the only way of shutting off the internal dialogue."

Seeing What Isn't There

We've save this for last, because this is the good stuff. We've been practicing these techniques for years now on our own, but found a good little book in our research that outlines much of what we discovered. It's called *Little Manual for Players of the Glass Bead Game,* by George Pennington. (Tisbury, Wiltshire, Element Books: 1983).

Try this: put two pennies on a table, equally lit, in the same position, about two inches apart. Look down at them, and unfocus your eyes by slightly crossing them. Do this by relaxing the eye muscles, not tensing them. The pennies will turn into double images as they move out of focus. By gently manipulating your eye focus, connect the shifting image of the left penny and the right so that it appears you are looking at three pennies. Keep working at it until you have aligned them perfectly. Then just stare at the middle image. It will seem brighter, more radiant than either of the "real ones." In fact, the side pennies might appear to become white or transparent.

Pennington has a very similar exercise in his book where you use your thumbs instead of pennies. We tried this, and like it even more. Hold your thumbs out in front of you, about two inches apart, and unfocus (cross) your eyes to create at first two "inner" thumbs, then overlap them to make one third thumb. This thumb will appear more lifelike than either of your "real" ones. It will seem to emanate life force. If anyone ever wants to know what the world looks like when you're tripping, have them do this exercise.

After you've gotten good enough to be able to maintain this for a minute or so, play with it. Manipulate the thumbs in different ways and see what happens. Try the same thing with penny-size dots drawn on a piece of paper. Use two different colors and combine them in the central dot. This two-colored dot (you'll have to see it to know what we mean) seems to float above the page that the real dots are drawn on. The possibilities are endless.

The magic of this technique is that the illusion appears more "real" than reality. This casts an interesting light on the dimension in which we live. Our physical reality and all that we see, may just be a projection from somewhere else — some source of everything. We play out life on a "holodeck" of sorts. By creating our own illusion, that of a third thumb for example, we come in direct contact with that interface.

Do pick up a copy of Pennington's book if you'd like to try more exercises, or his visual version of the *Glass Bead Game.* Or go back to Castaneda's *Journey to Ixtlan* to try some of Don Juan's techniques. The most all-encompassing source of visual hallucinatory techniques can be found in Pierre Derlon's *Secrets Oublies des Derniers Inities Gitan,* Editions Robert Laffont, Paris, 1977.

Chapter Two:
Sounds Good To Me

The most common way people get high today is through music. We are so inundated that we hardly realize the profound effect it has on our states of mind. Music has been shown to have marked effects on the ill, the emotionally disturbed, the mentally disabled and the profoundly insane. Music can increase the growth in plants or even the activity in yogurt cultures. As we all know by now, music — and sound itself — is a powerful tool for altering consciousness.

Sound has been abused by those who understand it. Muzak has been proven to make us buy things. White noise can increase productivity in the workplace. Annoying sounds emanate from certain areas of shopping malls to help corral people into the stores.

With a fraction of the knowledge needed to exploit sound in these ways, each of us can develop an extremely powerful tool for controlling our own states of mind and levels of consciousness. By either making music, creating sounds, or listening to the sounds and music of others, we can get very, very high.

How Sound Works

Sound is a wave form. Mathematically, in three dimensions, a sound wave looks like a stretched out Slinky toy. The frequency of the sound is represented by how many loops the spiral makes in a given length of wire. Sound waves affect us in a real, organic way. They are not just ideas. They are physical events. Sound waves enter through the ears (as well as through the rest of the body as vibrations) and move parts of our brains. Sound has a direct effect on the way our brain functions. It is a physical tool, in the shape of a spiral, that can enter through our ears and create waves in our brains.

Different sound waves have different qualities. A bell will create a very smooth, round wave — the open sound is thus soothing to the brain. An alarm clock buzz creates what we call a "sawtooth" wave, which looks like the sharp teeth of a saw. Its effect on the brain, then, is correspondingly uncomfortable.

Any shape of sound wave can also have any frequency. Certain frequencies will sound good together, and other ones will not. Sympathetic frequencies, the kind that sound good, usually share some of the spirals of the Slinky. There is overlap every few turns. In other words, each four turns on one spiral will correspond with exactly eight turns of another. The brain can recognize the patterning, and align itself fairly easily. If two frequencies seem unrelated to the brain, it will not know how to "fix" or resolve the frequencies.

The same is true for the overall rhythm of sounds. We can hear rhythm in repeating patterns. This is the way musicians can write their own music down on paper. They start by setting up rules like "every measure will have four beats." This creates a song with a repeating pattern of four beats. The brain has something to hook onto.

When the brain feels comfortable with sound, it allows the sound deep inside. This is the important part. Once a sound gets inside a person, the person naturally resonates with that sound. This is an organic resonance — it is more than just a "feeling."

You can resonate by producing sound or by just listening. The effects are different, but all quite interesting.

Making Sound

With nothing more than a pot and a spoon you can reach places you thought were reserved for monks. With a few other props, you can sing with the angels. But the first and primary musical instrument is the human voice. A voice is all you need to reach bliss.

The easiest way to start using your voice is by chanting sounds like mantras. We know, you do not like meditation. Fine. Don't think of this as meditation. The first obstacle to get over is the fear of making sound. Start by making sounds where you cannot be heard. (This is why so many people sing in the shower. They think that the noise of the water is drowning out their voices.) Go to a good, resonant place. If there is no empty cathedral or warehouse readily accessible, find a garage, a tunnel, or even a porcelain bathroom. Sit and listen for a while. Relax.

Lie on your back. Begin by watching your breath. Breathe with your mouth open. Then, very slowly, allow your breath to activate your vocal chords. On each exhalation, relax into a "huh" sound. Just feel the way the sound moves through your body. Make this as effortless as possible. Do this for as long as you can stand it. Your mind might start to move just from this.

Try standing. Tilt your head back, opening your jaw all the way. Allow a wide-open "hah" sound to come out. Hold the sound until you are out of breath (but don't force anything). Once you feel comfortable with these simple sounds, allow yourself to do a simple chant. Stand up straight, look forward, and make the sound "OM." Broken up into parts, the "OM" sound is actually "AH-OH-UUMMMM." Make this sound at various pitches.

Once you have experienced anything at all, take yourself through the next stages. Experiment. Try sitting, standing or moving. Use different pitches, sounds and tempos. Open and close your eyes. The possibilities are endless.

Chords

Next, bring your friends. Many people have experienced their first highs making group chords. Unlike the rigid rules of a junior high school chorus, the techniques of chording are very freestyle. Stand with a group of people — the more the better — in a big circle. You can do this anywhere. Each in your own time, make the "AHH" sound. Do not worry about singing in any standard harmony. Just sing out. Let the chord go on for as long as it wants to. Amazingly enough, most of the time everyone will stop simultaneously anyway, with no prodding. A chord can last ten minutes or an hour.

As with any soundmaking, the most important thing is to listen. Your consciousness will not change if it is not open. In this case, you must be open to the sound. This means you should relax and listen. Do not bear down on your own sound. Listen, and resonate with the sound that is around you.

Sound With Props

The best course at Princeton was labeled "Clap for Credit" by its detractors. It was taught by a genius, J. K. Randall, who showed us how to listen. He set up a table with kitchen utensils, made us each take one, turned off the lights, and told us to listen and make sound. It was as easy — or as difficult — as that. The results were amazing.

We have all been at parties that "de"-generated into improvisational jazz sessions in the kitchen. Try the same thing, except begin gently (and without being drunk). Listen to every sound. Create a fabric of resonances that intertwine with each other. You can graduate to tribal instruments like drums, kalimbas, flutes, and bells if you wish. But remember: you are not playing instruments in order to make music. You are just playing and listening.

The quality of this play should be like when a baby learns to make a new sound. It will repeat this sound for what seems like hours on end. The baby is simply fascinated by the way the sound *feels*. The baby is getting off on the sound.

This sounds too easy, we know, but look at every collection of monks, any tribe, or any group of babies. Sound is the way they alter consciousness. They chant, sing, or bang on things to get high.

The highest our friend Jamie ever got chanting was when he joined a group who performed the Balinese Monkey Chant (the Ketjak). Admittedly, not everyone has an Indonesian chorus in their backyard, but many universities now have international music as part of their curriculum. See what is available. Most teachers of ethnic music will let you join their classes whether you are a student of the university or not. You can certainly take part in extracurricular performances.

Tuning Forks

One slightly more organized, but equally effective, sound technique uses tuning forks to create resonance. You need to purchase a set of forks, one for each note of the scale. Buy aluminum ones because they are cheaper, and a little easier to use. Lay them out in front of you in order, from lowest to highest. Sit in front of them. The way to operate a tuning fork is to take it by the handle with two or three fingers, and strike the other end against your knee. Do not hit it against a table or hard surface, because the fork will ring a second, slightly annoying, tone.

Try the lowest fork with the lowest note. Hit it against your knee, and bring it about two inches from your ear. If you are not sure that you are hearing the tone, hit the fork against your knee again, and set the handle against your forehead. Hear that? The way to alter consciousness with tuning forks is to combine frequencies. Certain intervals work better than others. Try the lowest and highest first. They should be exactly an octave apart. Hold one in the left and one in the right hand, hit them against your knees, and bring them up to your ears. Try moving them about your head. Then try the lowest one along with the fifth from the left. Try many different combinations.

24

Other Instruments

The number of easy-to-use, mind-altering instruments out there is almost endless. Try bells, gongs, xylophones, chimes, drums, or anything that looks fairly resonant and easy to play. There are a few good books on making music. Most of them are written for nursery school teachers and can be found in the appropriate section of the library. You might also try *Music and Sound in the Healing Arts*, by John Beaulieu (Barrytown, NY: Station Hill Press, 1987).

Brain Synchronization

Synchronization tapes, also called the "Brother Charles" tapes, are not music, so they need a category of their own. They are part of a program designed to help people evolve their consciousness. The tapes available to the public are pretty powerful indicators that Brother Charles is onto something. This is not an endorsement of his spiritual program, however.

The tapes work by synchronizing the left and right hemispheres of the brain through sound. You must wear stereo headphones to listen to the cassettes. There are different cassettes to bring you to different brain states. The most basic ones are about $25 each, and available through MSH Association, Rt 1, Box 192-B, Faber, VA 22938 (1-800-962-2033). We have only tried one, called *Om Mani Padme Hum,* based on the Buddhist chant. It definitely works, bringing us to a deep meditative state within a minute or two. These tapes are more than just music. They "meditate" you, even if you do not know how. They were created to bring meditation to Westerners who do not seem capable of developing the patience to meditate the old fashioned way.

To really get benefit from these tapes, you might want to subscribe to the whole MSH program. You join by taking a course through the mail, in which they send you tapes and talk to you on the phone. They save the advanced stuff for their official students. The people we know who have subscribed to the course swear by it. Still, the vehemence with which they swear might make you want to think twice about "joining" anything.

Buying Music

Now that high fidelity is readily accessible on a decent Walkman, most anyone can purchase a high on cassette. The rest of this chapter amounts to a list of music that gets you high. We tend to stick to the more esoteric, tribal stuff. Anything Indonesian, African, Indian, West Indian or ancient usually works for us. Many people also get great results from electronic and New Age music. You can get high off any kind of music. We are sure there are people who get high off Duran Duran. If you have a favorite kind of music, that's fine. But chances are you are used to it in a way. If you have been getting off on Mozart for the last twenty years, chances are the patterns it creates in your brain are almost standard by now — euphoric, perhaps, but standard.

The way to use music to change consciousness is to bring new resonances to the brain. New rhythms and textures create new patterns. Thrown off-balance, even temporarily, the mind gets busy. It frees the consciousness to explore new territory. Live music, of course, is always better than recorded, but on nights where there is just nowhere to go, and nothing to do, turn to your stereo.

Go to the biggest or weirdest record store in your neighborhood and browse the shelves. Check the international section and the New Age records. The best 25 that we know of for altering your consciousness are:

1. Any good Buddhist "overtone" chanting. These guys sing more than one note at a time. The best we know of are the Gyoto Monks on Windham Hill Records.
2. The Balinese Monkey Chant. This gets pretty ferocious. In Bali, art and everyday life are one thing. The performers are just people, but boy can they make a lot of sound.
3. The Grateful Dead. Find a Deadhead and ask him to play you his favorite concert tape. Tell him you want to listen to "Darkstar" or "Morning Dew." Make sure it's from a concert near 1970-72, when they were still touring with the "wall of sound" ampli-

fication system. If you don't know the Dead, have an open mind. There's a reason they are still the #1 touring band in the country after 20 years. (Our friend Bernie says that "China Cat Sunflower" off the Europe '72 tour album gives an excellent head rush.)

4. Any good Dervish Music. Try the *Dhikr of the Halveti-jerrahi Dervishes*. This is music to spin by (see moving meditations).

5. African Drums. Play this loud and through speakers. Find *Drums of Passion,* which is African tam-tams, or any non-anthropological African drum recorded. The problem with the scientific ones is that they only play 30 seconds of each rhythm.

6. Bulgarian music. This is a relatively new rage (they used some in a TV commercial so it must be mind-altering). The Bulgarian Women's Choir has recorded two albums, *Le Mystere des Voix Bulgares Vols. 1 and 2.*

7. Brian Eno. We know. Eno. Not only does his name spell "one" backwards, but his *Ambiant* records (particularly #2 and #3) are stunning examples of how music, even when it's *intended* to do so, can alter your consciousness.

8. Tony Scott. You don't have to be meditating to audition his *Music for Zen Meditation* or *Music for Yogic Meditation*. Don't condemn this because it sounds like New Age stuff.

9. John McLaughlin and Pat Metheny. We put them in one category because they are both guitarists. Check out McLaughlin's *Shakti* and Metheny's *As Falls Wichita...* albums. They are not the kinds of recordings you would expect from guitarists.

10. *Yamantaka* is a collaborative effort of modern and traditional artists working with chimes, bells and gamelan to create the weirdest, most ethereal sounds they can. This one works.

11. Music of Native Americans. Some people report that these records bring out terrible feelings of guilt and remorse. Still, though there are not many natives left in America, there are numerous albums worth your while. Again, be sure the cuts are longer than a minute or two.

12. Real World Music is a branch of Virgin Records dedicated to recording traditional and modern music from around the world. Pe-

ter Gabriel is one of the producers of this series of fine recordings from Asia, Africa and Europe.

13. Iascos and Constance Demby wrote the music for the video *Illumination*, and have albums of their own that are equally evocative. This is new age type music.

14. "Marcey" is a woman who, after facing a life-threatening accident, began to create electronic music that has done everything from healing to bringing people out of body. Her tapes are available through her own company (PO Box 830495, Richardson, TX 75080, 214-690-3556). These compositions evoke a very different experience from most new age music, and bring the listener very close to the trance state Marcey was in when she wrote them.

15. *Music of the Pygmies* is a record of mostly chanting. The cover is neat, and the pygmies have very unusual voices, tones and rhythms.

16. Indian Music. Find any traditional ragas, kirtans, and bhajans, such as those on *Introduction to Indian Classical Music* or *Classical Ragas of India.*

17. Anything by Vangelis. People who like synthesizer music probably already know most of his work. His earlier recordings are more trippy than his later albums and film scores (avoid things like *Chariots Of Fire*).

18. *The Kodo Heartbeat Drummers of Japan* is pretty fabulous on CD, but the dynamic range is just a little too wide for cassette. These guys chant and bang loud. The cumulative effect is thrilling. Get the tape only if you cannot stand CDs.

19. *Holophonics Live!* is an album that was put out by the *Brain-Mind Bulletin*. It is a full dose of a wide variety of mind-altering sounds. Holophonics is based on the work of Hugo Zucareilli, who understood sound as a holographic experience of the mind. His sound effects experiments challenge what we thought were the limits of recorded sound.

20. Ray Lynch's album *The Sky of the Mind* has some excellent Tibetan bell music. The recording is great for opening up to sustained tones and resonances. Most any Tibetan bell music will be quite effective in bringing about changes in your mental state.

21. Steve Reich's music is often compared to Philip Glass's but is much better for our purposes because it doesn't make you insane. He takes a line of music, and slowly alters it as it repeats. The effect is not spacey — it is involving and awakening. You have to be conscious to listen to this music. Try *Tehillin* which is mostly voices.

22. Richard Burmer sounds pretty middle-of-the-road New Age to us, but he does seem to be a favorite among the people we know who use music to alter consciousness. His *Bhakti Point* is intended to be "a musical journey to an imaginary paradise."

23. Gamelan. This is music from Indonesia played on instruments that look like short and squat xylophones. The gamelan scale is different from the eight-note chromatic scale we are used to, and tends to retrain the mind into new patterns of awareness.

24. Haitian Voodoo Music. If you can get over the false notion that voodoo means black magic, you will find a treasure of mind-altering sounds here. Haitian drum music is very different from the African tam-tam mentioned above.

25. Wildlife. There are several good recordings of the music of the whales and dolphins that can bring out a tremendous feeling of compassion and warmth. Also try recordings of the sounds of jungles, rainforests and deep woods. Of course, these recordings are only the next best thing to being there.

Chapter Three:
Take A Deep Breath

The breath is a fascinating thing. It is one of the only processes in the body that can be either consciously or unconsciously controlled. That is, if you do not think about it, you will breathe naturally. You breathe this way in your sleep. Your breathing is as unconscious as your heartbeat or the function of your spleen. But you also have the ability to control your breath mindfully. You can hold your breath, breathe more or less deeply, more or less rapidly, through your nose or your mouth, in one way and out the other, in special rhythms — the list is nearly endless.

Because the breath can be either conscious or unconscious, it becomes a gateway between these two parts of yourself. Your breath is the link between your waking state and a myriad of other states of consciousness. By breathing consciously, you bring into current experience that which is usually reserved for the subconscious. Thus you gain easy access to a number of highs.

These techniques have been practiced for centuries in pranayama, the yoga of breathing. Current work in the field, dominated by Stanislav Grof, uses breathing for psychiatric therapy and "rebirthing." And since time began, children have been hyperventilating just for fun.

The following techniques are considered extremely dangerous by their practitioners. They are included here for reference purposes only. If you are interested in any of them, find a qualified instructor.

Pranayama

Pranayama is taken from two Indian words. The first, prana, roughly stands for the Indian equivalent of the Taoist chi. It means life energy, or cosmic energy. It is the stuff that makes everything go. Ayama means conscious control. Pranayama is the conscious control of the cosmic energies. One major access to the prana is through the air, so pranayama uses breathing techniques to develop a larger store of prana in the practicer.

Prana is believed to be conducted through negative ions in the air. (Later, we will consider ionizers and their effect on consciousness.) This is important to know, because the pranayama exercises will work better in an area more densely populated with these healthy ions. The easiest way to judge if air is properly charged is how you feel when you inhale it. You are not likely to find many negative ions in an office building or on a polluted freeway. On the other hand, if you do breathing exercises on a beach or on the plains, you will have far better results. Find the best place you can.

An excellent book on pranayama is B.K.S. Iyengar's *Light on Pranayama*. The best sources of pranayama practices you can do at home are in Andre van Lysebeth's *Pranayama: The Yoga of Breathing* (London: Unwin Paperbacks, 1979). Following are a few of the basic methods you can find in his book, or at the beginning class, ending in an advanced exercise that should bring you quickly into an altered state of consciousness.

A Pranayama Exercise

The point of focus in these exercises is the olfactory region at the roof of the first sinus cavity, just inside your skull. This is the place where air can go directly to your brain. To get a sense of this area, smell or imagine smelling something sweet like a flower. The place where you perceive the sweetness of the scent is the olfactory region.

Try breathing through your nose, allowing as much air to contact this region as possible. It will be helpful to "hold" (not with your hands but with the muscles in your nose) you nostrils open while doing so.

After you are confident that you are experiencing your breath in this way, try adding a visualization. Imagine that energy rises up along the back of your spine with every inhalation. It may eventually manifest as a warm, tingly feeling traveling up your back to your skull. You may want to visualize this as a color, light, a force — it does not matter.

Be sure to think of your abdomen as the motivator of your breath. Most of us use breath from our chests. This is shallow breathing. As you breathe in, your abdomen should expand. Do not force it to distend. If you imagine the air enters you like milk being poured into a bottle, you will see how air fills you from the bottom up. Eventually, you should begin to feel your lower back ribs expanding as you inhale, and coming together slightly as you exhale. If your breathing is tense, and this sensation is unavailable to you, consult Kristin Linklater's *Freeing the Natural Voice* (New York: Drama Book Publishers, 1976). The first chapters are a lesson plan designed to help you breathe this way. The Linklater technique is one of the best commonly taught methods for freeing up a channel for air.

So now you are breathing consciously, through your open nose, stimulating the olfactory center, and visualizing energy traveling up your spine. The last of the basic techniques to add on is called alternative nostril breathing. Quite simply, it means breathing in and out through one nostril, then in and out through the other. Do this using your right hand. Close your right nostril with your thumb, breathe in, then breathe out. Open your right nostril, and close the left one using your index and/or middle finger. Practice alternate nostril breathing, along with the other techniques, until you can do them without thinking.

Rhythmic Breathing

The first specific exercise a pranayama student learns is rhythmic breathing. Do not work too hard to get it right. This will only cause you to be more tense. Begin by exhaling through both nostrils. Then, alternatively breathe, counting "one one thousand, two one thousand," on the inhalation and "one one thousand, two one thousand, three one thousand" on the exhalation. In other words, breathe in a relaxed fashion, but with the exhalations taking twice as long as the inhalations. Alternate this rhythm back and forth, in and out through one nostril, then in and out through the other.

As you get better at this, you can try increasing the length of each inhalation and exhalation, as long as they stay in the same ratio of one beat inhaling to every two beats exhaling. This exercise, properly done, is extremely powerful. Do it sitting up straight, preferably on the floor.

Between Inhaling and Exhaling

Once you have mastered the above technique, try the following, more advanced practice of holding your breath. Start by doing everything listed above. You are now breathing rhythmically and alternatively, two beats in and four beats out. Now, when you inhale, retain the breath in your lungs for eight counts. That is, twice the length of an exhalation. If you feel yourself get tense, shorten the rest of your cycle. If you need to, just count one beat on the inhalation, four holding in, and two on the exhalation. Slowly increase the amount of time you can effortlessly hold your breath.

This place, between inhaling and exhaling, is where most people have experienced the more profound alterations of consciousness. After a while, it is as if you forget to breathe. You feel your skin almost start to make up for the fact that the lungs have stopped breathing. You also feel your blood circulate through your body in a different way.

Breath retention itself is an extremely advanced pranayama technique. You can practice this outside of class as long as you stay gentle and effortless with yourself. The trick is not to take one deep breath and hold it, but to breath deeply for a while, and just hold the last in the series of inhalations. For more advanced techniques, call the yoga schools in your area to see which offer pranayama classes, or consult Lysebeth's book.

Holotropic Breathing

This is a technique used in some of the post-psychedelic therapies. When LSD was legal, many psychiatrists used it to alter their patients' consciousness and help people redefine the arbitrary and sometimes limiting structures around their experience of life. A session would last several hours, and take the form of an acid trip with professional guidance.

When the best of these drugs became illegal, these doctors tried to develop other techniques which would provide as intense an experience of psycho-spiritual catharsis and resolution. Stanislav Grof and his wife, Christina, came up with something called holotropic breathing. They and other therapists have been using this technique for years now, with impressive results. Very similar techniques to theirs are also employed in a system called Rebirthing, which, as the name implies, involves reliving the birth trauma.

The Grofs do this technique in groups. They set up a large, safe room, play some evocative music, and tell their patients to breathe in a certain way. The patients go through the full range of transpersonal experiences, ranging from time and space alternation to visits with spirit guides. Some thrash about, some begin to sing and chant, some go onto past life regressions, and others just get very high. The Grofs hypothesize that holotropic breathing awakens some of the original anxieties experienced in the birth canal. Whatever stage of the birthing process you got caught in colors your experiences for the rest of your life. Holotropic breathing can help people explore these patterns in their thinking and behavior.

Rebirthers use very similar techniques, but in a one-on-one session. They do more hands-on work with their clients, helping them through the rebirthing process. Our problem with their technique is that, for many practioners, it is tied to a huge set of doctrines about human experience. These rebirthers seem to be promoting a way of looking at the world. This may just be an unnecessary adjunct to their technique.

The Grofs and rebirthers would insist that their techniques are for professional use only. They are the equivalent of LSD in their "dangers," both physically and psychologically. While there are no chemicals used in the holotropic technique, it does produce extreme physical reactions, ranging from involuntary movements to throwing up. Every therapist we consulted said not to put this technique in the book. Thus challenged, we felt obligated to provide you with the following information. Be advised that we cannot recommend you do this.

The Technique

Find a partner you trust. Someone who has some experience in these kinds of things. Remember, anything can happen. If you have ever done strong psychedelics, you know that set and setting are very important factors. For this reason, take the necessary precautions to insure that nothing will occur to upset you during or shortly after your session. Take the phone off the hook, be sure no one rings the doorbell, do not eat a big meal, etc. Take the same care you would take for a psychedelic experience. This *is* one. As with any of the techniques outlined in this book, do not do it unless you are of sound mind and body and have your doctor's okay.

The partner probably will not need to do anything but watch. He or she is there as a safety valve, and to give you a feeling of security. There is someone there to keep you from hurting yourself, to provide you a bucket to throw up in, or to put pillows under your legs if you start kicking the floor.

The technique itself is very easy. All you need to do is lie on the floor or on a futon on the floor. (You can fall off of the bed.) Lie on your back and play a tape that you would like to hear. Music you are unfamiliar with might work better, to prevent you from making patterned associations. We would also suggest music with no words. Let your partner find something for you to listen to. Turn off the lights, close your eyes, relax your body, and listen to the music. Then, begin to breathe more heavily than normal. Somewhat deeper, and somewhat faster. This need not be extreme. This is the technique. Just breathe deeper and faster than normal.

It is not important whether you breathe through your mouth, nose or both. Do whatever is most comfortable. If you forget to breathe deeply and rapidly, your partner should touch you to remind you to do so, but should not try to force you in any way. You are in charge of the experience. After about ten or fifteen minutes, you may begin to feel the physical effects of hyperventilation, such as curling up of the hands and toes, or tension in another region of the body. This is good.

The way through the tension is to keep breathing. Keep going. After a long while, you will push through the blockage you are experiencing. Grof's book, *The Adventure of Self Discovery* (Albany, State University of New York Press, 1988), explains in detail the nature of each of these tensions, and how they relate to blockages in one's experience of life. But this knowledge was gained through observation of holotropic sessions. One need not understand the varieties of holotropic experience in order to appreciate them when they occur. All in all, a holotropic session follows an orgasmic curve. It takes an hour or so, and bursts through about two-thirds of the way in.

The kind of blockage that can get dangerous is a blockage in the throat area. Grof assures us that the way through the accompanying respiratory difficulty is, as with all blockages, by accentuating the symptoms, and not by suppressing them. In other words, if you are experiencing a facial or neck tension, get behind the tension. If you are vocalizing, gagging or coughing, do some more. Your partner is there to support you through this in any way possible. Even just a hand on the shoulder to let you know he or she is there can help.

Resolution of the session usually takes care of itself in the period after the climax. If for some reason you are not allowed to peak, and the tensions you experienced are still happening, you must still push through them. For example, if you are experiencing tension in the hands, tense them intentionally. If you cannot, your partner should do this to your hands, or whatever part of the body is stressed. If the pelvis is in tension, for example, find a yoga pose like the cobra, or the bridge position, that accentuates the holding.

If you do pass through the climax stage, just rest for a while. Eventually, your partner should inquire if you are still experiencing tension anywhere in your body. He or she should gently press the areas, if any. This may retrigger the state of consciousness from your session. Repeat this process until you feel completely relaxed.

We cannot stress the power of the above technique enough. It is most definitely a full psychedelic experience. If you do not believe you can experience something as profound as LSD without LSD, you have not tried holotropic breathing.

Kidstuff

The breathing techniques you developed as a child still work today. Here are a couple of the things we used to do.

The Squeeze

Hyperventilate by breathing in and out deeply and quickly. After about ten breaths, your friend grabs you from behind and squeezes all the air out of your lungs as you exhale, holding you up at the same time. You will either get high or pass out. Your friend should watch your head as you hit the ground.

The Pressure Pinch

Squat, and take ten extremely deep and fast breaths. On the last inhalation, breathe in all the way, then close your mouth, pinch your nose shut and stand up quickly. Gently push out with the air in your lungs against your closed mouth and nose. Do not let the air escape. You will feel pressure in your ears and forehead. Exert pressure — *not so much as to make it hurt* — for ten seconds, then let go and exhale. Have someone around, because you may fall down.

For extra credit, precede this exercise with a minute-long, eyes-open spinning session. As soon as you are done spinning, squat and begin breathing.

High Altitude

Many people get high when they go to high places. Once you get up about 10,000 feet above sea level, you can experience remarkable alterations in your consciousness. Rather than driving up a mountain road, it is preferable to go up all at once, either in a helicopter or on a skylift. Most mountain ranges have facilities like this for tourists.

The vast majority of people who go to these places experience highs that they ignore. They assume they are sick, or merely inspired by the beautiful view. Those of us that understand consciousness, however, recognize the lightheadedness and accompanying clarity as something else. When you are sick, you experience a change in physical sensations, but you lose clarity of thinking. When you are high, you experience a physical change too, but thoughts seem to be clearer. Being open to what high altitude can do to you is half the technique.

So go with what you are feeling. It may seem subtle at first, but it will get very extreme, very soon. We have seen people weeping, laughing, dancing and even passing out from high-altitude consciousness work. If you start feeling too high, or like you are going to faint, just sit down and breathe slowly. It will certainly pass. Most of getting high has to do with being open to the experience. You can always regain control by going back to breathing and relaxing.

Do not complicate your high-altitude experience with the ingestion of any chemicals, even alcohol. This is extraordinarily dangerous, as chemicals will affect your body differently. The most intense chemicals we would ever take during a high altitude rush are tea and donuts. Just the caffeine and glucose will send you spinning.

After you are in your high-altitude altered state, observe your perceptual abilities. Look around you. Your vision and hearing will be sharp. Try talking and singing. Notice how different you sound to yourself, especially in comparison with the way other people and things sound. Feel free to do one of the meditations described in later chapters. Do anything you like, as long as it is not too strenuous.

The high-altitude high comes on subtly, but is very intense. Do not break it by engaging in extreme activities of any sort. Just walk or sit, look around, and breathe.

Negative Ions

Negative ions are in the air. They are healthy and cleansing, and are thought to transmit the energy of life and light. They occur naturally in the air, and are found in higher concentrations near the ocean or in open plains than they are in the mountains and lush woods. They are hardly found at all in cities, office buildings, or homes made of modern materials.

Metal neutralizes the charge of negative ions. Air that passes through a heating duct contacts the metal. By the time it gets from a furnace or air conditioner to you, it has no negative ions left. The unnatural, metal-framed places in which we spend most of our time act like Faraday cages, blocking out the negatively charged particles that give us vitality, clarity, and emotional sanity.

To replace the depleted negative ions — at least indoors — several machines called ionizers are available for anywhere between $40 and $100, or more. These are not just air purifiers or filters, but ionizers, which actually emit negative ions. In doing so, they trap dust, which falls to the ground near the ionizer. This dirties the floor but cleans the air. More importantly, they charge the air you breathe back to its natural state.

Ionizers work. They do not get you "high" in the standard sense of the word, but they do make you feel better all the time. Thus, they add to the overall high of life. If you do the other exercises in this book indoors — especially those that involve breathing — you should purchase an ionizer to get the maximum effect. There are hundreds on the market now, so you will have to use your judgment in picking out a good one. The factors to check are whether or not you have to replace parts, how much air the ionizer can handle per hour, warranties and price. Read the literature accompanying the particular unit. You should be able to get a sense of the company's priorities. The best units we know of are made by very small companies — usually one or two people — who care enough about their product to put their home phone numbers on the instructions in case you have any problems.

Chapter Four:
Sex

Good sex may be the most intense alteration of consciousness available to earth creatures. The sex act, through a kind of static electricity charged by friction, opposition, and attraction, literally creates the spark of life. Inseparable from this event is the experience of sex itself, a shedding of social values, increased intimacy, vulnerability, total honesty, and a moment of bliss, followed by an alteration of consciousness. This is the mystic experience.

We lose the ability to experience sex fully in several ways. First, we concentrate too much on our sex organs, and not enough on our total being. Reducing sex to the "contact of genitals" would be like reducing the experience of a milk shake to sucking through a straw. There's a lot more going on than that. We also limit our sexual experience because we are afraid to feel. If you are not in touch with your feelings during the day, you can't expect to suddenly let loose all your passion on cue. To experience sensuous, fearless sex, you must learn to experience life in a boldly sensuous way. But the biggest obstacle to transcendental sex, and the one really underlying all the others, is a sense of unworthiness.

We limit the possible joy of our sexual encounters because we feel we are not worthy of such an experience. This manifests itself in several ways. A man may think the woman's depth of passion is far greater than his own. He could never please her. He manifests this mindset in premature ejaculation. On the other hand, this same sense of unworthiness could cause him to be a brutish, uncaring lover. He assumes that if he tries to please her, he will fail, and resent his partner for this. The object of his game becomes to please himself while not pleasing her. Similarly, a woman's unworthiness may manifest itself in the belief that the act of sex is for the man's enjoyment, and not her own, because she is unworthy of an orgasm. Rather than make her needs known, she "puts up" with sex. Meanwhile, all she does is create resentment in her partner, who can't understand why she isn't satisfied.

Another way we manifest feelings of unworthiness during sex is by playing "Can you top this?" Couples strive for more intense orgasms through the use of leather, whips, chains, or poppers (amyl nitrate inhaled through the nose before orgasm), convinced that they are incapable of transcending sex on their own. They are addicted to orgasm, and believe its source is somewhere other than in the interaction between them.

Before we get too down on ourselves, remember this: most people don't have transcendent sex, even if they talk like they do. Chances are, the more they boast, the more they are really just compensating for the shallowness of their experience. Best of all, the good news is here — it's actually been here for a dozen centuries or so. For partners or even solo artists willing to accept the fact that sex is more than a bump and a squirt, an unlimited range of transcendental experience awaits you.

Some final words about this chapter. First, everything is expressed in terms of male/female energies. This is because the Tao and Tantric texts are based on that particular permutation. We assume you can translate most of these principles to gay and lesbian sex, or any other kind we might be overlooking. The following techniques might seem extremely technical, and some of them are. But even mastery of all the physical techniques in the world could never truly enhance sex without love. It has always been our opinion that the primary component of good sex is love.

Sex is transcendent only when the desire to express love and create pleasure is greater than could possibly be manifested on this plane of existence. It's transcendent because it has to be. Sex is an act of adoration. Even masturbation requires true self-love to be a transcendent act. If you believe that sex and love are two different things, and have a stake in that belief structure, try a different chapter.

The Tao of Sex

The Tao of sex is based on the same principles as the Tao of anything. Briefly, it is that everything manifesting itself on earth is some combination of the two essential forces, yin and yang: Yin is the feminine energy, and corresponds with the moon, the night, and the earth; while Yang is the masculine energy, and corresponds with the sun, the day, and the sky. The familiar yin/yang symbol indicates that these two forces are continuously moving, even dancing with each other. The only constant is their circular movement and change. The fuel for this movement is life energy, or *chi.*

The Tao of sex concerns itself with balance of the male and female energies. Sex becomes a living, working example of the yin/yang in action. The better a couple learns to circulate chi, the more nourished they are by each other's energies, the more "electricity" they create, and the more heightened their level of consciousness becomes. The principles for attaining better circulation of chi during sex are pretty simple:

1. Ejaculation is not the highest sexual pleasure for a man. In fact, the Taoists believed that a man should not ejaculate but once in five or ten sessions. The semen is to be considered an essential and precious life fluid. The older a man is, the more he should retain it. Ejaculation is also something that should never be forced. One need not "change gears" towards the end of a session in order to move toward orgasm. When the body needs to release semen, it will do so.

    In practical terms, the idea would be for the man to take pleasure in the moment he is in, rather than goal-orient himself to orgasm. If he can resist the temptation to move toward orgasm, or learn to control it when the opportunity presents itself, he will reach new heights of sexual bliss. As in any meditative or physical discipline, it is in the moment after you push yourself one step farther that your consciousness goes one level higher.

Prolonged lovemaking may seem difficult at first, especially for men who equate sex with ejaculation, or have gotten used to a quickie to help them fall asleep. The techniques to delay orgasm are simple. The easiest, called the "locking method," is simply to withdraw the penis whenever the urge to ejaculate occurs. Wait until the urge subsides, then enter again. Another, called the "squeeze" technique, is even simpler. When the man feels the urge to ejaculate, he firmly presses the point between his scrotum and anus. Another method, although not Taoist in origin, is for the man to tell the woman when the urge to ejaculate has come. She, in the straddling position above him, must lift herself off him and tightly squeeze the penis with her thumb and forefinger, just below the tip. When his erection begins to subside, she should mount again. A newer, popular method is to gently pull the testicles down and away from the body when the urge to ejaculate is felt.

Prolonged lovemaking, as far as we're concerned, is anything over twenty minutes. But allowing yourself to go for two or three hours can lead to ecstasies far beyond what you may have thought were possible.

2. Hand in hand with the man's retention of semen is an increased focus on the woman's satisfaction. She should be allowed to have orgasms as often as she wishes. Also, as the "house" of the sexual energy, she is the focus of the sexual act. (This also helps get attention off the penis and ejaculation.) Taoist doctors went through great pains to determine the various physical signs a woman exhibits to indicate her state of arousal. We think most receptive lovers can figure this out for themselves. Then, if a woman still isn't getting exactly the kind of arousal she needs — be it harder thrusts or whatever — she can simply ask verbally. Talking during sex is an excellent means of communication.

3. Thrusting techniques are the staple of a Taoist lover's diet. They are described at length in various texts, both in terms of depth and motion. Most popular is the nine-shallow one-deep method,

which involves nine shallow thrusts followed by one deep thrust, and then repeats. You can also try five shallow and one deep, or even two shallow and one deep if it doesn't excite uncontrolled ejaculation. As far as the quality of motion, *The Tao of Love and Sex* (Jolan Chang, New York, Dutton, 1977) has some excellent translations from the *T'ung Hsuan Tzu,* by seventeenth century physician Li T'ung Hsuan:

1) Strike out to the left and right as a brave warrior trying to break up the enemy ranks.
2) Move up and down as a wild horse bucking though a stream.
3) Pull out and push in as a group of seagulls playing on the waves.
4) Use deep thrusts and shallow teasing strokes, alternating swiftly as a sparrow picking the leftovers of rice in a mortar.
5) Make deep and shallow strokes in steady succession as a huge stone sinking into the sea.
6) Push in slowly as a snake entering a hole to hibernate.
7) Thrust swiftly as a frightened rat rushes into a hole.
8) Poise, then strike like an eagle catching an elusive hare.
9) Raise and then plunge low like a huge sailing boat braving the gale.

(Chang, p. 50)

Vary thrusts to prolong excitation over long periods of lovemaking, or to ward off ejaculation.

4. The Taoists are also very concerned with the vital fluids: saliva, vaginal secretions and semen all contain vital life energy. In kissing, the couple should try to exchange saliva ("jade fluid"). The woman's yin will be nourished by the man's yang fluid, and vice versa. They also consider a woman's vaginal fluid ("yin essence") to be a vital nutrient for balancing a man's yang energy.

5. The Taoists list too many positions to include them all here. Let it suffice to say they believe in doing it lying down, side-to-side, sitting up, woman on top, man on top, standing up, from behind — they even describe positions using small mirrors, so that lovers can watch their expressions as they move through the various stages of ecstasy. Chances are you can find most of these positions yourselves; referring to diagrams during lovemaking is

decidedly unspontaneous. Remember that variety is the key, and the positions you feel uncomfortable about trying may just be the ones that open new doors.

Tantric Sex and Yoga

Tantric sex is based on the idea that life energy begins at the base of the spine and in the genitals. Sex provides a channel for that energy. The object, though, is not simply to expel the life energy through the sex organs, but to help it move up through the various chakras. Most people have experienced a feeling of heat emanating from the middle of their chest during sex. Westerners think of this as love emanating from the heart. According to Tantra, this is one of the channels through which the sexual fire flows.

To pursue Tantra, watch for workshops being offered in your area, or read *Sexual Secrets: The Alchemy of Ecstasy*, by Nik Douglas and Penny Slinger (Rochester, VT: Destiny Books 1979) or the more general treatment in Marcus Allen's *Tantra for the West*, (San Rafael, CA: New World 1981). Following are some of the basic Tantric beliefs, and some things to try at home.

Preparation

Preparation, both mental and spiritual, is essential for transcendental sex. Meditate calmly before sex, visualizing in whatever way you wish as your loving, sexual energy rises from your spine and genitals through your chakras and out the top of your head. Also meditate on your lover as a deity whom you are about to worship through the sex act.

To prepare physically, do some simple yoga asanas (exercises). Try doing a head stand or shoulder stand (against a wall if necessary) and concentrate on the energy flowing downward toward your head. You might also try the cobra position (see Moving Meditations) except with your mouth wide open and your tongue sticking out and down.

Sex as Prayer

The Tantric texts usually describe making love from the point of view of a yogi praying to his goddess. The sex act is an act of devotion to the goddess, who is embodied in the female partner, or "yogini." Except in moments of supreme ecstasy, when concentration is impossible, the yogi is completely focused on pleasing his lover. Making love is a moving prayer, an offering to the insatiable female deity.

The woman's role is surprisingly similar. She, too, is to find her ecstasy in serving her partner. The best way for her to do this is to allow herself to be consumed by her passion. She mustn't hold back. Tantra accepts the fact that the male and female response curves are different, and calls for the yogini to abandon any of their obstacles to letting go. She does this for the sake of the yogi, who is dependent on her release for his own. So to sum this up, both the man and the woman are focused on *her* pleasure. He strives to give her joy, and she, in receiving it as fully as she can, gives the man his pleasure.

The Tantric path of ecstasy is really a manipulation of the orgasmic curves of the two partners. Almost like tacking a sailboat back and forth to go in the desired direction, the couple uses each partner's rise and fall to move two steps forward, one step back. The process is actually pretty simple to understand, even if it requires a good deal of stamina to execute. If you have a willing partner, and a few good hours, try this one.

The only necessary techniques are control for the man and the ability to release for the woman. The Tantric techniques for control include most of the ones listed above in Tao. They also suggest concentrating on the sensations of the whole body, rather than just the genitals. Imagine energy flowing up through your spine and out the top of your head. To help this energy flow, try rolling your eyes up (don't strain). The focus is on raising energy up. It is also important for the man to realize it is not he alone who is investing energy into the sex act. Making love (when it is more than coital masturbation) is about a flow of energy, not just a release. True love is not something you spend or something you get. It is at once both a circulation of energy and an equilibrium. For both partners, steady breathing is a must. For the man, it will allow him to regulate his potentially spasmodic body functions. For the woman, it will keep her from bearing down or holding on.

The Tantrics call this sexual technique "Riding the Wave of Ecstasy." There's a complex description of how this works in *Sexual Secrets: The Alchemy of Ecstasy,* but the basic idea is pretty simple. It's just a matter of alternating between excitor and excitee. After a good period of foreplay and mutual excitation, you begin to have sex. Both participants focus their attention on the woman's pleasure. As the woman reaches her first climax, the man holds back on his own. He absorbs the energy released by her orgasm, and as soon as her excitement begins to subside, he brings her back up. After she is moving up, the couple rises together. Now it is the man's turn to approach climax, but just as he gets close to the point of no return, the woman draws him up into the next realm of excitement. (Had she not climaxed, she would not have the energy to bring him up.) Now it's the man's turn to refrain, then the woman's, then the man's again. The key exchange in this process occurs at the moment that the excitor becomes the excitee, just after each orgasm or energy leap. You go through this process four times, counting by the woman's orgasms. Each female climax brings the couple to a new chakra. By the fourth one, we are in the throat/head areas, and the bliss is unreal. You can forget about the techniques now. Climaxes blend into climaxes, as partner blends into partner. Self-consciousness dissolves as both lovers are absorbed into the ecstasy they have together created.

Something A Little Easier, Perhaps

One can experiment with the Tantric energies without having sex. A friend of ours tried this exercise with a girl in his kundalini class, and was convinced he was in love with her for weeks. Actually, what the yoga process made available to him was a direct experience of the depth with which he could give and receive love and life energy.

The objective of this exercise is to circulate energy. First, do a few yoga postures separately, concentrating on raising your own energy level. End these individual warm-ups with a more exerting motion or "breath of fire" (see Moving Meditations). As you come together, sit cross-legged facing each other, and hold your hands up, palms facing your partner's pattycake style, but not touching. Leave them about six inches apart, and look into your partner's eyes, or up at his or her third eye (between the eyebrows), as long as you're both doing the same thing. Now imagine a circle of energy flowing from the base of your spine, and out through your eyes or third eye, and hands, to your partner. Stay like this for at least ten minutes, using your own and your partner's chakrik energies to keep your hands up when they get tired. If your mind drifts, just bring it back by sending as much energy as you can to the other person through the third eye and the hands. You may also begin to experience other connective energies with your partner along various chakras, creating a feeling of warmth in the solar plexus, throat, or lower abdomen.

Next, without breaking the energy fields you've created, and keeping your hands the same distance apart, very slowly move them in small circles, as if wiping steam off a piece of glass between you and your partner. This will feel something like a mirror game. Whenever you get out of "synch," and the distance between the hands changes, you should feel a strange magnetic tug pulling them back together.

After you've done this for a few minutes, start to play with the energy field you've created. Try pulling your hands slowly apart from your partner's, or closer to them. Try leaning in with your body, too, and then out. We know people who have used this exercise as a seduction technique, and it probably works as one, but those who use it that way will certainly miss the real joy of this Tantric practice.

Orgasm As Bliss

For all the orgasm retention we've been talking about in this chapter, one would think it were an unpleasurable experience. Clearly, it is not. There are a few simple techniques you can develop in order to experience fuller, more crashing orgasms that create ecstasy for the body, mind and spirit all at once.

The first is diaphragmatic breathing. Most of us don't realize this, but we stop breathing when doing something difficult, or which causes us tension. This sets off a chain of physical and mental

48

responses which remove us from the direct experience of whatever we're doing. If you see a gun or firecracker about to go off, your reaction will be to hold your breath, squint, and tense up. To experience full orgasm, you must learn to let go of these reflexes, which are largely anticipatory in nature and which deny the joy of a given moment. The orgasm will come in its own time. The more you try to help it come along, the less there will be when it arrives.

To practice breathing from the diaphragm, lie on your back and relax. Watch the air go in and out. As you inhale, you abdomen should expand, and not contract. As you exhale, the abdomen collapses. After you've got this down, you can try to experience the expansion of your lower back ribs as you breathe, then your whole lower back down to your anus, all breathing with you.

Try breathing this way until you've settled into a rhythm, and relaxed your entire body. Then let your partner masturbate you or perform oral sex on you. The partner should start gently caressing other parts of you, slowly working toward your genitals. Intercourse is too advanced for this stage of the game. If you like, you can do this to yourself without a partner, keeping your masturbating hand as relaxed as possible through this. Massage oils and lotions work well for this. As your excitation increases, you may add some sound to your exhalations. A "huh" sound produced from your lower abdomen works well. Throughout all this, the key is not to tense up anywhere. Places to watch are your anus, shoulders, neck, hands and feet. Stay completely relaxed. Most of all, do not help in any way, or move yourself toward orgasm consciously. Don't even worry about acknowledging your partner, if any, for now. There's time for that later. Just breathe. As orgasm approaches, the temptation to hold onto your breath or a part of your body will magnify. Use your exhalations and sound to dissipate this need, especially during the orgasm itself. After it's over, follow through by staying absolutely relaxed and breathing diaphragmatically. You will be in physical bliss *and* a highly altered state of consciousness for quite a while.

This is a relatively easy method of achieving an amazing high, and it's as accessible as your hands or lover. For more advanced techniques, as well as a whole program designed to enhance sexual response and orgasm, see *Total Orgasm* by Jack Lee Rosenberg (NY: Random House, 1973.)

Chapter Five:
Effortless Highs:
Meditation

Sooner or later, most people in search of higher consciousness turn to meditation. While probably the most subtle of the methods available to you, it is also the most effective and long lasting. Unlike skydiving, cassettes, or isolation tanks, meditation is essentially propless. It can be done anywhere, at almost any time. These facts have made meditation our method of choice.

First, because meditation requires no paraphernalia, you are completely responsible for your experience. Propped highs, like those derived from mind machines, lead you to identify your pleasurable state of mind with a given machine. In reality, the machine is not the experience, any more than a car is the experience of a road trip.

With meditation, the illusion of reliance on something outside of yourself is much less common. In this way, it is the furthest of these techniques from drugs, which create a very strong mindset of dependence. Meditation, simply put, is choosing to get high and then doing so. No tricks, no gimmicks, no effort. This is probably why it is so hard for Westerners to believe it works. "I don't have to *do anything*?" Nope. In fact, the knack of meditation, if there is one, is learning how to do nothing — or if you must do something, watch yourself doing it rather than get caught up in results or judgments. Western thought dictates that effort leads to results. While this may be true for industry or even weightlifting, it is not true for getting high through meditation.

Your Western goal-orientation can be exploited during the first stages of meditation, though, so don't worry too much about it. If you are meditating "in order to get high," that's okay. As you meditate, your goal will probably vanish before your eyes. You'll be in a state of bliss where reaching toward fun, or anything other than where you are, will seem like a worthless, off-centering effort. Getting started in meditation for a specific reason is fine. Just be willing to watch that reason change if it wants to.

The "reasons" to meditate are your mind's way of permitting the activity. The receptionist needs to feel justified in putting this on your daily calendar; let the following suffice: meditation improves physical health by slowing your pulse, lowering your blood pressure, deepening your respiration, improving your vision (as well as your other senses), regulating the functions of nearly all your organs and glands, and adding years to your life. It improves your mental health by reducing stress, improving concentration, dissipating neuroses, providing deep relaxation, curtailing depression, augmenting synaptic transmission, and making you smarter, calmer, and quicker. Meditation also feels good, gets you high, leads to spiritual advancement and might even make you enlightened.

The way meditation works is rather simple. It takes your consciousness past the receptionist and out of the office for a while. There are two ways to get out of the receptionist's control: get it busy, or put it to sleep. Then you can walk right past it and outside. You don't even have to sneak. Float right up and out through the ceiling if you feel like it. There are no longer any rules. The methods of getting the mind occupied are varied. Some involve chanting a mantra, focusing on an object like a candle, or even trying to work out a complex problem or paradox. Putting the mind to sleep is simple: watch for long enough, and it will just conk out. Whenever the mind presents you with an issue or problem during your meditation, simply nod and say "that's nice" or "that's thinking." Keep doing that, not allowing your consciousness to attach to any of the thoughts that arise, and you will soon move to a place far beyond the plane of concious thought.

In this chapter, we have outlined a good number of meditative techniques. The one you choose is unimportant. Do whatever seems the best for you. This chapter is dedicated to still meditations. All you need to do is sit down somewhere and begin. In the next chapter, we outline moving meditations, which involve a simple or complex motion of the body.

There are four main meditative paths. One appeals to the intellect, and is called contemplation. Rather than escaping from the mind, you occupy it with your own agenda. The mind then assists your ascent. Another path is through the emotions. Through devotion to God or a master, you experience perfect love. You see how the object of your devotion is perfection. Slowly, you are able to apply this vision of perfection to the entire universe, including yourself. Mantra meditation involves the repetition of a word or phrase, either vocally or mentally. The sound acts as a vehicle for your consciousness to travel to new places. There are also a great variety of unstructured meditations, ranging from simple mindfulness to thinking about a particular problem. The final goal of all of these processes is to bring the meditative state into your daily awareness. Life itself becomes a meditation. You are always conscious, always high.

To prepare for meditation you need to do a few things. First, make sure you are in satisfactory physical condition. Meditation involves sitting still for long periods of time, sometimes on the floor or a meditation pillow. Hatha yoga (described in the next chapter) was invented to prepare the body for meditation. You might want to do several weeks of asanas before beginning, or do them before each time you meditate. Any of the techniques outlined here can also be done in a good chair that keeps your back straight, so don't worry too much about being physically fit.

Regularity is important. You should meditate at least once a day, and at the same time each day. It takes about a month for any activity to become habitual, and you want meditation to become a part of your life. It's time to quit window shopping, sit down, and commit to the quality of your life experience. You are not "spending" an hour of your day. You are "getting" an hour of what life's about. You deserve it. When you feel like not meditating, realize that this is your mind coming up with an excuse to leave things as they are. Meditating is not hard. Sitting down for an hour (or even twenty minutes) is hardly an act of great discipline, although the mind will convince you that it is, or that meditation is painfully boring. It is not. An hour of bad television is boring. Soaring outside the boundaries of time and space is thrilling. Believe us, it works.

Another way to create regularity is to meditate with a group or class. Having other people meditating around you helps reinforce the notion that what you're doing is good. It also makes it harder to get up and quit. A group meditation creates a field of energy in which it is easier for each meditator to break away from normal consciousness.

We also suggest you set aside a place in your house or apartment where you only meditate. You don't need to build an altar or invest in a Japanese bonsai garden. You might want to buy a meditation pillow or some incense, and establish one corner of a room as your meditation space. You may hang a particularly inspiring photo or painting in this place. Creating a meditation space not only gives you a place to call "home," but also helps you feel more committed.

When doing almost any meditation, you will get an urge to stop. You might feel bored or impatient, or suddenly remember something you had to do, or someone you had to call. Tough. Sit it out. Almost as soon as you let those thoughts pass, and recommit to your meditation, fantastic new depths are reached. It's like a spiritual second wind. The way to push over these "humps" of resistance is by *not* pushing. Do not force yourself to stay in meditation. Rather, relax further into the meditation. Exhale deeply, feel your forehead relax, and begin your particular mantra, thought or technique again.

This cycle, meditation leading to miscellaneous thought leading to boredom or impatience and then back into deeper meditation, is the process by which you move into fuller states of consciousness. You are not just going in circles, but rather ascending a spiral staircase, where each successive step corresponds to a step directly beneath itself. It may seem like you are in the same place as before, but you are actually one level higher.

So, remove all your expectations, read through the following techniques, pick one, and go for it. If you prefer to work with a teacher or meditation group, look in your local yellow pages under Meditation Instruction, or purchase a copy of *Meditation* magazine, which has a large listing of meditation schools and groups in the back. Ram Dass's book, *Journey of Awakening*, (Bantam Books, 1978) dedicates over a hundred pages to a directory of groups that teach meditation and retreat facilities.

Simple Meditations

Watching the Breath

The simplest meditation is to watch your breath. All you need to do is find a comfortable, upright sitting position, either on the floor, on a pillow, or in a chair. Close your eyes, and begin to notice the breath passing in and out of your nostrils. Your mind will invariably wander, but as you notice yourself thinking about something other than the breath, gently bring your attention back to the sensation of the air passing through your nose.

Candle Meditations

This process is the same as the breathing meditation, but instead of focusing on the breath, you focus on a candle flame. Place a candle a foot or so in front of you, and just look at it. Again, as you notice the mind wandering, gently bring your awareness back to the flame. This meditation is slightly more difficult, because it requires a greater effort at focusing your mind on a single point.

Third Eye

The third eye is a point on your lower forehead, just above where your eyebrows would meet. This point is used in many Indian meditations, as well as this one. Third eye meditations are noticeably transcendental. One often feels quite altered for several hours afterwards.

For this meditation, find a tree, and sit or stand five to fifteen feet away from it, depending on its size and how you feel. Imagine a silver thread connecting your third eye with a specific point on the bark of the tree. Concentrate on that point on the bark and your connection to it. Do this for 45 minutes. Two variations on this meditation involve chanting the sound "OM." If you are seated, simply chant the sound, one long "OOOOMMNM" on each exhaling breath. If you are standing, do the same chant, but also slowly step three or four steps towards, then three or four steps away from the tree as you breathe and chant. Your arms should be at your sides, with your palms facing back.

Sublime

The next time your are in a truly beautiful place, like a mountain range, or waterfall, try this simple practice. Sit somewhere comfortable, facing the most majestic vista you can find. For example, face the peak of a mountain, or the top of a waterfall. Put your wrists on your knees, and gently tap your index finger and thumb together, once a second or more. During this, as slowly as you can, open and close your eyes repeatedly. The process of getting your eyes open should take thirty seconds or so, and after they are completely open, you should begin to close them again, in a controlled movement taking just as much time. Do this for at least fifteen minutes.

Oriental Paths

Tibetan Buddhism

The Buddhists have developed some of the least "religious" seeming meditations. They often involve no mantras, statues or specific ideology. Here is one of the main techniques of the Tibetan Buddhists, and probably the sort you will most likely encounter if you seek out a Tibetan meditation center.

The rules are simple; the practice is less so. All you do is sit, breathe, and watch thoughts go by. As soon as you realize you are having a thought, label it "thinking." You may use the word "thinking" if you like, or just acknowledge that you had a "thought," and move on. To refocus, concentrate on your exhaling breath. If you are distracted by a sound or body sensation, do the same thing: return to watching your breath. You should

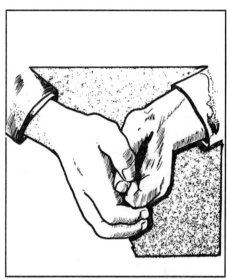

breathe through both mouth and nose. Don't try to control the breath; just watch it, experience the sensation of it exiting your mouth. Once you have re-centered, you can let consciousness of your breathing fade away. Do this in a seated position, with your eyes open, for at least thirty minutes at first. Although your eyes are open, you aren't looking at anything in particular. You should let your eyes rest on an area of the floor five or six feet in front of you.

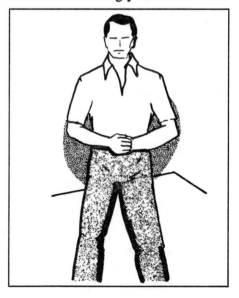

Another form of this meditation alternates between the above technique and a walking meditation. Do the sitting meditation for

45 minutes, then, for fifteen minutes, walk around the room or garden, concentrating on the sensation of the soles of your feet against the floor, instead of your outgoing breath. Your head should be down, and hands clasped gently, left fist in the right hand as shown. Place your clasped hands on your navel, and walk. Again, whenever a thought comes into your consciousness, label it "thinking" and return your awareness to the sensation of your feet against the floor. After fifteen minutes of this, go back to the sitting meditation again.

This meditation opens up your awareness to the space between your thoughts. Often, we believe that we are our thoughts; this is not true. Our consciousness is a continuum into which individual thoughts may penetrate, like the ticks of a clock, into the silence around them. This silence, this peace, is the state of pure awareness.

The Hindus

Bhakti

Although it seems somewhat inaccessible to Westerners, Bhakti meditation is worthy of mention here, if for no other reason than it is the principal form of prayer in Hinduism. It is a devotional practice in which the meditator concentrates on an inspiring god or guru. By devoting one's entire thought and energy to the "ishta," as the object of devotion is called, you can free yourself of all other worldly attachments. You are eventually able to see the perfection, or God, in all things and people, even yourself. This is the way many Christian churches work. Through complete devotion to Jesus, you are enabled to see Jesus in all creation.

Bhakti practice consists of chanting something like "Hare Krishna, Hare Krishna, Krishna Krishna, Hare Hare. Hare Rama, Hare Rama, Rama Rama, Hare Hare." Rama and Krishna are two Hindu deities. If you're not afraid of cultish behavior, (and you probably should be) visit your local Hare Krishna center on a Sunday afternoon and try taking part in their devotional singing and dancing.

The interesting thing about devotional highs is they take into account the fact that highs often seem to come from an external source, like drugs or even a mantra. These practices exploit our sense of un-worthiness and our belief system that we are incapable of manifesting higher consciousness on our own. The devotee identifies all positive experience with the ishta. Only later is the practitioner able to feel the ishta within.

Still, devotion is an excellent high, as long as you feel secure that the object of your devotion won't turn on you, or prove somehow un-worthy, as many spiritual leaders and evangelists have. Devotional activities also include charity work, like cooking food at a shelter for the homeless, or donating time to the Red Cross. Whether or not these activities can be called "meditations" is debatable. The idea here would be to keep in mind as you work that your whole being is dedi-cated to serving God, the deity in others, and the holiness in yourself.

Kundalini

Kundalini is a kick-ass form of Hindu meditation and yoga. The yoga postures and movements are discussed in the next chapter, but should be done in combination with the meditation techniques out-lined here. The Kundalini have done the most research of all the Hindus, and base all of their practices on an intricate system of chakras, breathing, astrology and brain patterns. The Kundalini believe that life energy begins at the base of the spine, then moves up through the various chakras, past the open window of the third eye, and out through the last chakra on the crown of the skull. Whether or not the Kundalini model is exactly accurate, be forewarned: these meditations are very powerful. They involve manipulation of energies from deep within you, and can produce some shocking states of con-sciousness, from euphoria to out-of-body travel. Thus, it is advisable to find a Kundalini teacher if you choose to pursue this deeply. You can contact the Kundalini Research Institute at 800 N. Park Ave, Suite 5, Pomona, CA 91768, or the 3HO Foundation, International Head-quarters, House of Guru Ram Dass, 1620 Preuss Road, Los Angeles, CA 90035.

Usually, a Kundalini session would consist of physical exercise, followed by meditation. After that, the meditator takes time to experience a deep relaxation. Group songs usually follow, and then a prayer ends the event. We recommend preceding the following two meditations with one of the Kundalini exercises in the next chapter.

Sah Tah Nah Mah

This is one of the first meditations a Kundalini student learns. Sit on a pillow or on the floor and close your eyes. Concentrate on the third eye as you slowly chant the sounds "SAH TAH NAH MAH." Use the melody of the first four notes of "Mary had a little lamb." (MA-RY HAD A....) Begin by chanting in a normal voice. After five minutes, go into a whisper. Then, after another five minutes, do the mantra mentally. As you chant each syllable, gently tap each of your fingers against your thumbs. The index fingers on SAH; the middle fingers on TAH; the ring finger on NAH; and the pinkie on MAH; then repeat.

If you have trouble concentrating, or experience any uncomfortable physical symptoms during the meditation, focus on each sound of the mantra passing down through an opening on the crown of your skull and out again through your third eye. When you are finished, gently stretch before opening the eyes.

Sat Nam

This mantra is an abbreviated form of Sah Tah Nah Mah. We include this meditation because the first time our friend Sarah tried it about eight years ago, she went out of body. Needless to say, she was on a relaxed high for a week or so afterwards. Again, if this works for you, please seek out a real Kundalini yoga teacher. If these exercises are to be done every day, they should be done correctly, and as part of a planned program.

The exercise has several parts:
1. Five minutes: Sit, inhale through puckered lips to make a whistling sound, and exhale through your nose. As you inhale, imagine the sound reverberating at your third eye.

2. Two minutes: Change your breathing so that you inhale through the nose and exhale, whistling through the puckered lips. On inhaling, think of the sound "SAT" and on exhaling, think of the sound "NAM."

3. Three minutes: Lie on your stomach, put your palms on the floor next to your chest and push up, arching your back. (This is not a push-up. Do not pivot at the feet. Leave your thighs on the floor, arching your back.) Breathe as you did in part 2. Stare at a point on the ceiling directly above you.

4. Three minutes: Relax, exhaling, and roll onto your back. Close your eyes. Pull your knees into your chest and clasp your arms around them. Pull your head up between your knees, and chant the sound "NNNNNNNNN."

5. Five minutes: Rest, by lying on your back and crossing your legs. The legs are crossed as if you were sitting up "Indian Style."

6. Two minutes: Sit cross-legged. Put your hands on your shoulders, thumbs behind and fingers in front. Swivel your torso, leading with your elbows, left and right like the inside of a washing machine, pivoting at the spine. Inhale as you go left, and exhale as you go right. For the second minute, change your position so you are sitting on your heels, with your knees in front of you. At the end, take one last deep inhalation, hold it in, and exhale, proceeding to step 7.

7. Five minutes: Lean forward over your knees until your head touches the floor. Allow your hands to slide back toward your feet, palms up. Relax as far as you can.

The Relaxations

It is in the final relaxation that you feel the full effects of these meditations. After either one of these meditations, try the following deep relaxation technique.

Lie on your back. Imagine energy flowing up from the base of your spine all the way past the window of your third eye and out through the top of your head. With your eyes closed, imagine the slow mantra "SAH TAH NAH MAH" four times as you inhale slowly through the nose and hold the breath in long enough to complete the mantra. Exhale more quickly and with a little sound of air against your lips, as you imagine the faster mantra "WUH GROO." Your mind may wander from the mantra and breathing technique, so if you realize this is happening, bring yourself back to the practice.

We can't overemphasize how powerful this technique can be. When you are finished, it might be a good idea to hum a little tune or random notes to yourself before opening your eyes. We would also suggest gentle stretching before you try to stand.

The Kabbalah

Kabbalah is the much misunderstood and much underestimated mystical branch of Judaism. Do not expect to learn much about it at most synagogues. While Judaism, because of the way it is popularly conceived, is not the first place most people turn to find transcendental meditation techniques, those who do are often surprised by how much Jewish mystics understood about states of consciousness.

Shin Mem Meditation

This is a short, easy meditation with quickly observed effects. You alternate between making the sound SHHHH and the sound MMMMM. Hold each for fifteen or twenty seconds then switch to the other. What this meditation does is alternate your consciousness between the chaotic white noise of "shh" with the higher, focused, and directed "MMM" sound. The kabbalistic tradition states that the way to higher consciousness involves just briefly experiencing higher states, so that they can be readily integrated into normal life. The alternation between the two sounds of this meditation does just that. You only need to do this meditation for a couple of minutes.

Alphabet Soup

In *Path of the Kabbalah*, David Sheinkin outlines an ancient meditation technique based on the Hebrew alphabet. The letters of the Hebrew alphabet are thought of as more than just representations of sounds: they are mystical symbols. Each has its own special resonance. All you have to do is pick a letter (any Hebrew text or lesson book should have them all). Stare at the letter, and meditate on its shape. Once you have the letter committed to memory, close your eyes and continue to visualize it. Another form of the meditation is to imagine sculpting or chiseling the letter out of stone. Keep sculpting until only the letter remains in blank space. The most difficult of the techniques is to attempt to imagine the letter as black fire, and the background behind it as white fire.

If these techniques resonate for you, contact a Kabbalistic institute if you can find one. There are places to study in New York and Los Angeles. Otherwise, find some good books and translations and explore it yourself. The Jews spent hundreds of years traveling with books and no teachers, but managed to do a pretty good job of preserving the mystic texts, even if you have to go digging through the back shelves of bookstores in order to find them.

Chapter Six:
Moving Meditation

Like sitting meditations, moving meditations attempt to free consciousness from the limitations of the mind. Since movements of the body are controlled by the brain, learning new movement patterns retrains neural pathways. For example, if you are nervous, but engage in calm movements, your mind will settle. Likewise, if you engage in transcendental movements, you will get high.

Each of the following moving meditations functions in a different way. Tai Chi Chuan is a martial art based on the I Ching, and teaches control of Chi energy through slow, constant movement. Kundalini is a form of yoga that raises energy from the base of the spine through to the higher chakras, transforming lower and sexual energies to mental and spiritual ones. Sufi movement meditations range from sensory awareness to whirling dervish dances which bring the dancers into a state of rapture, one with God. The Feldenkrais method is the father of modern movement awareness techniques. It enhances movement through expanded consciousness, and widens consciousness through better movement.

As with any technique outlined in this book, make sure you are physically fit enough to try it. In giving these warnings, we are reminded of the time a student approached a Tai Chi instructor and asked, "My knee hurts when I move it like this — what should I do?" To which the teacher calmly replied, "Don't move it like that."

Tai Chi Chuan

Tai Chi Chuan is the first and best martial art for consciousness purposes. This ancient movement technique provides the basis for all other martial arts forms. If you are interested in studying martial arts, begin with Tai Chi. If you are not interested in studying martial arts, Tai Chi is also excellent for the health of internal organs, regulation and improved awareness of the flow of chi energy throughout the body, increased intuitive understanding of the I Ching, and better posture, coordination and endurance.

Most teachers do not teach Tai Chi as a fighting technique. They teach a "form," consisting of somewhere between 60 and 120 movements, depending upon the style. The individual movements have names like "carry tiger to the mountain" or "wave hands like clouds." As far as our friend Denise was concerned, she was learning an easy, slow, cool-looking dance. One year into training, she was mugged in New York. Her hands instantly flew into a movement called "white crane spreads its wings." She had struck her attacker once in the gut with her elbow, and again in the face with relaxed fingers before she even realized she was being threatened. She never knew "white crane spread its wings" could be used in that way, and probably couldn't use it the same way consciously, but she immediately gained new respect for the pretty movements she was practicing.

What keeps Denise involved in Tai Chi, however, is the way it makes her feel. Doing the Tai Chi form is one of the surest ways to get altered positively every time. After two minutes on a good day, or twenty minutes on a bad day, your arms and legs feel weightless as they float through space. Your mind is fixed on the motion, which never stops. Your hands control a ball of energy, chi, that seems to emanate from every part of you. At times you shake, tremble, cry or laugh, but you are always left extremely calm, clearheaded, and behaving like the person you always wished you could be.

It is close to impossible to learn Tai Chi without an instructor. You can't know if you are doing the movements correctly until you understand them as motions, and not positions drawn or photographed in a book. Tai Chi is kinetic, not static. Still, here's an exercise that moves internal energy, while leaving the body in one position.

Horse Stance

We won't say this isn't a taxing exercise, but the results are immediate and extraordinary. There will be three or four moments when you want to quit. Don't.

Stand with your feet pointing straight ahead, shoulders' width apart or wider. Keeping your back straight, bend your knees so they stay in the direction of your feet. (Do not let them buckle in.) You should now be in the position of a person riding a horse. Slowly raise your arms in front of you, and hold them as if you were carrying a huge beach ball. The arms are rounded, the palms facing you, about eye level. The fingers are spread, including the thumbs, and point towards each other, about six or eight inches apart.

As you stay in this position, imagine a ring of energy flowing though your arms, past the gap between your hands, and around your back. You can imagine it as light, water, or anything that works for you. Stare at a point between your fingers on the wall or in the garden in front of you. Now stay in this position for twenty minutes. This may sound crazy to you, but it's not. A 99-pound weakling can do this. Fat people can do this, too. It is not an exercise of muscle strength. What keeps the arms up is chi energy. What brings them down is lack of concentration on the flow of that energy. There will be some difficult moments during this exercise. Push through them by relaxing further, and concentrating more deeply. It is at precisely these moments that you have the opportunity to get very high. Sing, moan, cry, tremble and sweat, but keep your arms up.

Kundalini Yoga

Kundalini is also a technique that is best learned from a teacher or in a group practice. This form of yoga deals with very powerful energies, so it's the ideal yoga to use for altering consciousness. The high energies put into play, however, make it all the more important for you to be doing the exercise correctly. If you like the following practice, seek out a qualified teacher before ingraining any bad habits and possibly doing damage to yourself.

The Kundalini are the more intellectual branch of India yogis. They have elaborate explanations for how each of the exercises work, and plan long sessions of yoga, meditation and prayer. They would argue that these exercises do not work properly out of the context of a fuller Kundalini practice. We have found, though, that even when done infrequently these exercises can provide a sense of great alertness and well-being. That alone should help motivate anyone trying the techniques here to seek out further guidance.

Breath of Fire

This is a basic constituent of many of the Kundalini exercises, but can be done independently of them too. Sit comfortably, with your back straight. Breathe in and out through the nose only, in quick, short contractions. Use your abdomen to control the breath. Simply pull in the navel to expel air, and relax it to inhale. Do this as rapidly as you can, leaving your whole body relaxed except for your abdomen. You should have a box of tissues nearby, because Breath of Fire tends to clear out your nostrils. Do this for a minute at a time, until you can sustain it for longer. When you are finished, proceed to one of the Kundalini meditations.

A Simple Kriya For Strengthening the Aura

(Adapted from *Kundalini Yoga/Sadhana Guidelines*, Kundalini Research Institute of the 3HO Foundation, KRI Publications, 1978)

Stand with your legs spread. Lean over and place your palms on the floor, about two feet apart. Let your head relax down. Now raise your right leg behind you, without bending its knee. Raise it so the right foot is the highest part of your body. For one to two minutes, do "pushups" in this position. (Bend your arms, then straighten them; bend then straighten.) Then place the right leg back on the ground, and repeat the whole exercise with the left leg up.

Now sit either cross-legged or in an easy half-lotus position. Put your left hand straight out, palm facing right. Cross your right hand under and behind the left wrist, clasping the left hand from behind, both palms facing right, fingers interlocked. For two minutes or so, breathe deeply, raising the arms up a foot or so as you inhale, and back down to directly in front of you as you exhale. On the last inhalation, stretch your arms straight up, and relax in this position.

Lastly, put your arms directly in front of you, palms facing each other about six inches apart. For three minutes, breathe deeply and rhythmically, swinging your arms directly out and behind you as you inhale, and back to the front as you exhale.

Dervishes

The whirling dervish dances developed by the Sufis produce a state of consciousness unlike any other we have known. They are said to have been invented spontaneously by Sufi Saint Jalal ad-din ar-Rumi in the thirteenth century. He had been mourning the death of his best friend, and passed by a goldsmith's shop. He began to chant

"Allah" to the rhythm of the goldsmith's pounding hammer, and started to spin wildly in the street. The pure ecstasy he is said to have experienced in that moment is what Sufi dancers are reaching for in their spinning.

Unfortunately, there are few practiced Sufi masters around today teaching this stuff. Still, you can practice the technique on your own. Contact a Sufi Order (through Sufi Order, PO Box 396, New Lebanon, NY, 12125) if you wish to pursue the theology. They probably won't teach you to dance for a while though.

The Sufis believe that we are held down by worldly cares, locked into an inferior reality by our lower selves. The only salvation comes from consciousness of God. The following moving meditation incorporates this Sufi doctrine, leaving you feeling like a pure channel of energy — almost like a tornado: spinning and frictionless, formless, except as the interface between two differing fields of psychic pressure.

The Dervish Dance

Find a room or space with nothing you can bump into or fall onto. Use your judgment and don't get hurt. Put your arms out to your sides, the right palm facing the sky, and the left palm facing the earth. Imagine energy from God and heaven coming down from above into your right palm. It passes through your body and down through your left palm, into the earth. As you concentrate on this, spin in a counterclockwise direction. If you do it correctly, using the energy current to spin you, you should not get dizzy. In the words of Rumi:

> "A secret turning in us
> makes the universe turn.
> Head unaware of feet,
> and feet head. Neither cares.
> They keep turning."

(Jalal ad-din ar-Rumi, *Unseen Rain*, trans. by Coleman Barks and John Moyne, Threshold Books, 1986, in "With the Whirling Dervishes," Jannika Hurwitt, *Gnosis*, No. 11)

Japanese Zen Archery

It would be close to impossible to teach or even fully explain archery in a book, even if written by a Zen archery master. Kyudo, as it is called in Japanese, is a very focused form of moving meditation that allows the archer to experience the oneness of mind, spirit, and body by practicing to stay exactly in the moment. One of the main ideas here is not to think about hitting the target. The archer concentrates on the form of the movement, which is a set of very distinct positions: raising the bow, raising the arrow, pulling back, etc. One does not "shoot" the arrow at the target. The target and arrow are already joined. One releases the arrow and lets it find the center of the target. If it misses the target, it is because the archer got in the way.

The arrow, bow and target are indicators of one's inner state. For example, if the arrow wobbles, the archer is wobbly and off-center. In this way, unlike most other moving meditations, you are provided with a barometer of your progress. Almost like a psychic biofeedback machine, archery allows you to experiment with different states of consciousness, and directly observe their extension into physical reality.

The best way to begin to learn Zen archery is to take a good weekend or week long retreat with a master instructor. Courses are listed in New Age or martial arts magazines. Good, accessible instruction is available year round at Ryuko Kyudoju (4220 19th St., Boulder, CO 80302).

The Feldenkrais Method

Moshe Feldenkrais developed a series of exercises called "awareness through movement." Ostensibly, it is a system of exercises that improve your ability to move by heightening your awareness of the way the body works. This is not limited to the physical relationship of joints to bones or tendons to muscles. The Feldenkrais method also concerns the relationship of the mind to the body. It is in exploring this interface between intention and movement that these exercises provide access to strange levels of consciousness.

Often, a Feldenkrais exercise will begin by testing the range of motion of a certain part of your body. You will then do a simple movement that helps teach you how this body part works — not a stretch, but an awareness exercise. When you retest the range of motion, you will find it has greatly increased. Much more astonishing though, you will learn how to do the exercise mentally — not even moving — and get the same results. If you like the following exercise, you can find a Feldenkrais class in most cities, especially through acting schools. One of the best things about this system is that it is very easy to do, and it provides tangible evidence of its effects.

A Feldenkrais Exercise

The rule with these exercises is don't push. Nothing in Feldenkrais should ever hurt. Stand comfortably. Put your right arm directly in front of you, parallel to the ground. Now for the test: see how far you can turn your body to the right, without straining at all. Remember a place on the wall so that you can mark how far you have rotated. Now the exercise: gently and slowly move your arm (still parallel to the floor) to the right, as you turn your head to the left. Bring them both back to the center, and off to the side at the same time. Nice and easy. After doing this ten or fifteen times, retest how far you can rotate to the right. Now do the same exercise, moving your arm to the right and head to the left, while you keep your eyes fixed on a spot in front of you, causing them to move to the right side of your eye sockets. Retest your rotation, and see how much you've improved.

Now the amazing part: raise your left arm directly in front of you, and test your range of motion in a rotation to the left. Now, *imagine* doing the exercises you actually did with your right arm. First imagine moving your head to the right and arm to the left fifteen times. Remember the sensation of doing that on the right, and translate it to the left. Test your range of motion again. Now imagine doing the second exercise ten or fifteen times (the same as the first but keeping your eyes fixed forward so they swing left in the sockets). Again, test your range of motion. It will be just as improved.

This exercise, admittedly, is not enough to get you high, but it does indicate the path of Feldenkrais's work. In the more advanced exercises, your mind moves to some pretty bizarre places, as your perception of your body changes drastically. It is an intensely physical high, wherein you become acutely aware of the essence of motion. By exploring the interface between mind and body, you will gain access to a new place in your consciousness.

Chapter Seven:
Look Ma, No Hands!

A rush is the easiest high to recognize. We have all had them, recognized them, and even sought them out. They are all short-lived, and usually not very enlightening, but they are fun.

The lowest rung on the ladder of street drugs are those that produce short rushes and nothing more. In the sixties kids sniffed glue, in the seventies they used poppers and Pam in a plastic bag. In the late eighties, cocaine developed into freebase and crack, which produce shorter, more intense rushes. The trend of drugs away from sustained euphoria and towards quick rushes is alarming, but only natural for a western culture where bigger and sooner is always better. In a society where we equate sex with orgasm and education with a diploma, this is to be expected.

Likewise, most of our entertainment takes the form of fast, intense, experimental catharsis. Even our most successful movies are more like amusement park fantasy rides than anything else. The highs in this chapter are entertaining rushes. Here, we are more concerned with immediate results than process. Many of these techniques are dangerous — danger seems to be a primary component for most rushes — so take necessary precautions.

We remember a guy in high school who used to hang lights for the drama club. He always got a kick out of climbing on the lighting grid with no ladder or safety net. Occasionally, he would lose his balance and hang precariously by one hand until he could swing himself to safety. Afterwards, he would always say he felt "great." Danger feels good. Those of us who do not put ourselves in danger, often enjoy watching others do so. Thus we've created the careers of Evel Knievel and a few thousand other stunt performers and circus artists. Few of us watch trapeze artists for their grace. When the final drumroll begins, we watch to see whether or not the muscular young man is going to complete his triple flip or come crashing to the ground and break his skull. The moment he lets go of the first trapeze and takes to the air — the moment he has committed to the stunt but not yet completed it — is the source of a danger rush.

A spectator rush, though, is far different from experiencing the thrill directly. Following are the easiest and most accessible rushes available. They fall into two basic groups: falling rushes and exhilaration rushes.

Falling

Many of us have dreams of falling or flying, in which we actually experience the same kind of rush that we would get hang-gliding or parachute jumping. The other ways we imitate the experience of falling is with roller coasters and downhill sports like skiing and sledding.

Skydiving

All we can explain about skydiving in this book is what it feels like. You simply must take a set of lessons in order to skydive without dying. They are not very expensive, and, if you are somewhat coordinated, you can usually be jumping from an airplane within a couple of days. The only difficult things about skydiving are jumping and landing. Once you conquer the instinct that tells you not to jump out of an airplane, you are on your way. Take a lesson or two on how to hit the ground, and you're ready to go.

The skydiving high is perfectly structured. It goes something like this: You prepare by checking and rolling up your parachute. You feel an intense appreciation for the craftsmanship that went into this piece of silk, knowing that your life will be depending on it in just a few minutes. Then you step into a small airplane and take off. You sit in this small craft, in full knowledge that this plane exists solely for the purpose of jumping out of it. In fact, everyone around you is part of an insane group of people that spends their money and time jumping out of airplanes for fun. Someone might tell a story about "that guy last year whose chute got stuck." Great. After a while, everyone gets quiet. The plane just keeps going up and up. And up.

By the time they open the door, all you want to do is go home. You don't care that you've already spent your money on lessons. You just don't want to die. You are persuaded to move towards the door and you look out. You swear this plane is flying higher than any plane you've ever been on. Is the pilot sure he's over the landing spot? It doesn't look familiar...

Then, for some reason, in a moment you can't remember, you jumped from the plane. Just when you decided not to, something inside jumped out, and your body followed. Panic. There is no up or down. Everything is moving. You are tumbling. Count. You were supposed to count. You need to be a certain distance from the plane before you pull the cord. Where did everybody go? You want to go home.

Finally, you pull your cord and the unexpected happens. You go straight up. You are yanked up like a yo yo. The rush begins. Your face is somewhere down in your stomach. Your whole body is buzzing. You don't know if it feels good or not. It's just really fast, and really weird. Then, at last, everything stops. Peace. You look up. The chute is open. You look down — whoops, maybe don't look down, not yet anyway. You notice that you can hear for the first time. The wind rushes in your ears, but compared to before, this is heaven. You swing and float, float and swing. You remember to breathe. The adrenaline is still pumping, but you don't need it anymore. Except for the heartbeat at your temples, this is bliss. This lasts a good long while.

Soon the ground approaches. It doesn't seem to come that fast. The landing should be easy. You find a nice grassy place, steer the best you can, get ready to bend your legs like the instructor said and BAM! Ow! Harder than you thought it was going to be, but nothing's broken. You're alive. You just want to sit for a moment and look up.

You just jumped out of an airplane, and for no other reason than to do it.

Hang-gliding

Like parachuting, hang-gliding is a sport where the realization constantly hits you that you are doing something dangerous for the pure exhilaration. In gliding, though, you have a bit more control over your experience. It's a little harder, and somewhat more dangerous because you usually jump off rocky cliffs rather than into clear air. But you are dependent on your own skill, which for some is a necessary component of a good thrill. While parachuting, you are at the mercy of your rip-cord and gravity. In hang-gliding (and in the more guided forms of parachuting) you are more the master of your experience. A glide is also a great deal longer than a parachute jump. A jump lasts a couple of minutes. A good glide can last an hour.

The best way to get started gliding is to take a guided tour on a two-man glider. There are a number of instructors who will take passengers in their gliders with them. You pay forty or fifty bucks for a ride of a half hour or so. This is great fun because you don't have the responsibility of steering the contraption, but you get one hell of a ride.

Unlike parachuting, hang-gliding is done from a horizontal position. This allows you to look down much more easily. It also makes you feel more like you are flying rather than just falling. You move forward, not just down. Take-off is a little different, too, in that your role is much more active. In hang-gliding, you must make a running start towards the edge of a cliff, then leap off.

Hang-gliding requires a few more lessons than parachuting, but is eventually cheaper and a little more natural. Once you find a good spot — Aspen has some of the best — you can just bring your glider and go. The scenery is usually a little better too, because you have mountains around you rather than just open fields. Still, you don't get the exhilaration of free-fall — unless your glider breaks; but then that'll be the end of you.

Rollercoasters

Companies like Six Flags and Disney come out with new rides every year, each designed to disorient you in a new way. Some use water, others use lights, and others even show movies to you as you drop. All of these rides do essentially the same thing: allow you to fall fast.

Our favorite rollercoasters are the old ones made out of wood. These are scarier to me for several reasons. First, they make noise. Second, they are not gliding smoothly on metal tracks, but wobbling precariously on old wooden slats. At any moment, it seems, something could come loose, and the coaster cars could go careening through the railing and out over the park. Old coasters work by gravity. Like in a parachute drop, you experience a slow ascent which builds to a peak... then, out of nowhere, the great fall begins.

Many metal coasters have more intense drops, or even complete loops, but the experience is different. It feels more controlled. Still, in terms of pure motion, metal coasters provide more extreme experiences. Six Flags now boasts a coaster in which you stand rather than sit. There is a metal loop-de-loop coaster in nearly every American city, and numerous small-radius spirals that are only possible on metal coasters.

Disney's Space Mountain is also a pretty intense coaster experience. Space Mountain is a "Space Odyssey"-styled roller coaster completely enclosed in a huge dome. It is a roller coaster ride in the dark, with projections of stars and galaxies on the walls and ceiling. What makes the ride effective is that you have no idea what's coming up. You cannot see the drops as they approach. (Playland in Rye, New

York has a vintage coaster called the Dragon Coaster which does much the same thing. This old wooden ride has a tunnel near the top in the shape of a dragon. Inside, it is dark, and before you are completely out of the tunnel, you are descending the steepest drop.)

These coasters indicate some of the ways to get high on rollercoasters of any kind. The methods involve affecting your sight, your breath, or both.

Eyes Closed

Easier than it sounds. Go through an entire rollercoaster ride with your eyes closed, and completely relaxed. Do not tense up no matter what. Breathe evenly, and stay relaxed. If you hold the safety bar in front of you, be sure to do it without clenching. This is a more intense experience than we can describe.

Hyperventilation

On the way up, breathe as deeply and quickly as you can. As you reach the top of the first drop, hold in one last breath as deep and hard as you can; then as you begin to fall, let the breath go.

Another technique is to do something like holotropic breathing on the rollercoaster the whole ride. We have tried this, but cannot recommend it because we had mixed results. Just breathe deeply and quickly through the whole ride. Try to start as soon as you get into the car, so you are already a little buzzed when you start moving. Be VERY careful getting out, then stand holding onto a railing before walking down the exit ramp. It's very easy to pass out or throw up from this one.

Fixed Focus

This is cool. Pick a point in the air just in front of you and stare at it. (Check the chapter on meditation for how to do this.) You are looking into empty space. The easiest way to find this place is to put a finger a foot or so in front of your face, focus on the finger, then remove the finger without unfocusing your eyes. You should feel a little cross-eyed, but not strained. If you can make it through the first few drops without looking at anything, you will be in a very altered state of consciousness for the next few minutes. Try to maintain this state even after the ride is over. Don't talk for a few minutes. Just observe everyone and everything around you. Walk slowly off the ride and into the thick of the crowd.

Sensory Deprivation

Ride the coaster with your thumbs closing the little flaps over the holes in your ears. Your other fingers should be on your forehead, and your palms over your eye sockets. (Make sure your fingers are against bone and not your eyes so that you do not get injured.) Do not scream. Breathe through your nose with your mouth closed if possible. When the ride comes to a stop, slowly remove your hands. Again, stay quiet for a while after the ride.

Looking Up

This one is tricky. It only works on rides where you don't need to hold onto a lap bar. Clasp your hands behind your neck, and lean your head back into the cradle that your palms form. Bring your elbows forward to support your jaw. Do not arch your back. Keep it well supported in the back of your seat. Look straight up at the sky for the entire ride.

After you have gotten used to these techniques, try combining them and see what happens. Use care, especially in guarding your neck and spine, as well as getting off the ride when you're done.

The Sports Rush

Any time that emotions and great physical sensations go together, there is an opportunity for a high. Sports are a tribute to the link between the body and consciousness.

Running

There are a number of good books on running safely. They outline proper equipment and techniques. One of the best is *The Runner's*

Handbook by Bob Glover and Jack Shepherd. Nearly anyone can run and get high pretty quickly. Long-distance running releases endorphins into the bloodstream. Endorphins get you high. The potential problem is that runners get addicted to these endorphins pretty fast. If a week goes by when they are too busy to run, they get quite depressed.

Work Out

Aerobics and workouts work in very much the same way. A good, low-impact aerobics class can get you high. Each time you experience an endurance threshold, push through it. At each new level is a slightly different state of consciousness. Usually, during the exercise itself you are too focused on the activity to concentrate on your state of consciousness. Next time you work out, rather than going back to work or cooking dinner, take a long walk outside, or take a quiet sauna. With this kind of high, you need to soothe yourself immediately afterwards.

During exercise, your brain orders extra chemicals like adrenaline and endorphins to support you. When you suddenly stop the exercise, these chemicals remain in your blood. These chemicals are surplus, and are not immediately metabolized. The more extra chemicals in your blood, the higher you get. But you need to be receptive and relatively quiet for this to work. Try following an intense workout with a meditation or one of the other techniques in this book.

Competitive Sports

Most of us have not engaged in competitive sports since high school, and we are missing something. Participation in sports is one of the only ways we are allowed to exhibit our animalistic aggressive natures. The mammal within us is invited to surface. This does not mean you have to get rough. It does mean you have to cut loose.

Winning feels great. If you wrestle someone about your own weight and skill, you will notice a strange thing happen to you. At first, you think you are participating in a sport. You have learned certain moves, know the rules, and are attempting to pin your opponent.

But shortly into the match, the combination of your physical effort and drive to win unleashes an inner strength. From nowhere, a will to defeat your opponent emerges. Even if the match has no meaning outside the ring, it feels as though you are involved in a life-or-death struggle. Your primal instincts take over. Hopefully, your techniques are automatic. You shouldn't have to think about them. All you need from your consciousness at this point is will and endurance.

When you start to do extremely well in any competitive sport, something even more strange begins to happen. Pro basketball players describe a visual effect that takes place when they are playing their best. They say that everything around them appears to be moving in slow motion. They have all the time in the world to think about what they are going to do. This is more than a rush; it is a moving meditation.

The best sports to try are ones that involve direct interaction with an opponent. Confrontational sports more easily awaken primal energies. Try sports like hockey, football, basketball, boxing, or soccer. They should be endurance sports, that require you to be "on" for sustained periods of time. This way you force your body and mind to acquiesce to your instinctual competitive impulses. You have no choice but to get a rush.

Chapter Eight:
High Tech Highs

For several thousand years, the avenue to altered states was ritual and religion. In the past three decades it was replaced, at least in the West, by chemicals. The current frontier in brain research, however, is technological. "Brain machines" provide effective, controlled methods of reaching a variety of altered states, by manipulating and "entraining" the brain to reach particular wave patterns. To do this, brain machines use sound, light, and/or electromagnetism.

Since the 1920s, scientists have known about the existence of brainwaves, and over the following decades, they labeled them according to their frequencies: beta, alpha, theta and delta, in decreasing order. Beta is the brain's state of waking awareness. Alpha is a relaxed state, often used for healing and biofeedback, or as a first level of hypnotic induction. Theta is the meditational state. It is profoundly relaxing, and is often accompanied by faint visual imagery. Delta state is the deepest one we can get to so far. This is the brainwave of deep sleep and out-of-body travel.

Most machines work by creating some kind of phase distortion. For example, a note of a certain frequency is played through one ear, and a note slightly out of phase is played through the other. The resulting beat patterns are heard by the brain, which attempts to synchronize itself with that frequency. Add flashing lights at the same or resonant frequencies, and the effect is supposed to be augmented. The most recent additions to the brain machine arsenal are electromagnetic impulses, delivered to the brain by electrodes attached to the head or earlobes. More specific brainstates are also being explored by researchers like Michael Hutchison, who are attempting to map multiple parameters of the brain states of selected individuals so that their states of consciousness can be recreated in other people.

In almost all cases, the machines promote hemispheric synchronization. Rather than being allowed to work as two separate entities, the left and right halves of the brain are harmonized (in almost exactly the manner that Brother Charles or Robert Monroe use in their audio cassettes). The resultant "whole brain thinking" allows for enhanced learning, greater relaxation, behavior modification, better energy and even periods of euphoria: highs. (Ironically, they have also been used successfully in treating chemical dependency!)

Indeed, the most amazing thing about brain machines is that they get you very noticeably altered. They are not subtle like biofeedback machines. Put on a headset, and within minutes you will know you are in a different state. If you stay relaxed enough, you should be able to maintain your clarity for several hours after a session. Ideally, you will also gain the ability to reach a desired state of consciousness without the machine at all. Still, many people buy these machines for the visuals alone. While most machines actually produce only white light, users report hallucinating a series of multi-colored psychedelic images, usually associated with a feeling of euphoria. This is one reason why so many brain machines are being bought.

But they are fairly expensive. The prices of these units range from a couple of hundred to a couple of thousand dollars, but we are not altogether convinced that the expensive ones perform better anywhere but in the laboratory. Your choice of machine should depend solely on what works for you. No two brains are quite alike. Some people respond more to visuals, others respond to sound, or electromagnetic impulses. You need to try before you buy, unless you are wealthy enough to make your purchases by trial and error. The best way to sample all of the machines that are available is to attend one of the whole life or New Age expositions, where nearly everything on the market can be sampled for free.

The best of the brain machines are programmable and flexible. Rather than having just a few settings, they let you program an entire session. This way you can decide, for example, just how long you would like to be in alpha state before you move to theta, and so on. You also gain control of which parameters you wish to change and how gradually they should move.

The most expensive of the popular units is called DAVID (digital audio visual integration device). It is a professional sound and light machine, with probably the highest quality goggles (they're lined with special incandescent bulbs). There are synthesized effects in the machine's memory, as well as inputs for tapes or a microphone for a therapist. It is even equipped with some rudimentary biofeedback devices, so it can play back in the rhythm of your own heartbeat.

The DAVID Jr. costs about $900, and is portable. While it is not as flexible as the DAVID machine, it does provide the same types of sounds, and similar features. Its visuals are on a less expensive electroluminescent panel.

The DAVID Jr. unit also has something called the "Ganzfeld feature": a blank viewing field in the color of your choice. The Ganzfeld effect is in some ways a more profound deprivation than darkness. By stimulating the brain with a constant, unchanging visual field, you can attain the "blank-out" effect, whereby you lose touch altogether with the visual apparatus. This is not seeing blackness, but rather not seeing at all. There is a machine called "The Theta One" (which costs only $150) that features just a Ganzfeld effect and a brain synchronization tape.

One of the most programmable of the machines around so far is called "Mindseye," which is an audio-visual synthesizer, capable of playing back up to three hours of programming. At about $800, we would recommend it only for veteran mind-machine operators. It is quite complex, and designed more for programmers than users. If you are interested in advanced brain research, you probably already know about this machine. Otherwise, begin with a smaller model.

One of the easiest ways to get started is with a unit called "Inner Quest," a relatively inexpensive ($500) yet flexible machine. It also works with sound and light, and features a built-in Sony Walkman cassette player. Similar to the Inner Quest is a unit called MC2 (available for about $350 through Light and Sound Research, 6991 E. Camelback Road, Suite C-151, Scottsdale, AZ 85251, 602-941-4459). It boasts the same features for less money. Most other light and sound machines fall into this general category. Again, try them for yourself.

The other main category of brain machines incorporates a pulsed electromagnetic stimulation of the brain. It sounds dangerous, but so far it's still legal (although one of the machines requires a prescription). Brain machine pioneer Michael Hutchison backs a unit called "Alpha Pacer II," available for about $500, which uses sound and light in addition to cranial electro-stimulation. Robert Anton Wilson, in his review of these products (*Magical Blend,* July 1989), highly endorses the "Endo-Max" machine, which costs about $200, and is extremely portable. It uses only electro-stimulation and audio. Both of these units have been used to treat chemical dependency and seem to work something like modern acupuncture: an electrode is attached to an acupuncture point, then a charge is passed through the point to another one. The sensation is a light tapping.

Hutchison also recommends renting access to a machine called "Lumatron," which works by photic stimulation. (To purchase privately, the machine would cost $7,900, but it includes a four-day seminar.) Invented by Dr. John Downing, the machine works by stimulating the brain with short bursts of light at varying, but particular wavelengths. It is supposed to help regulate the hypothalamic discharge rate, and eventually balance the neuroendocrine system.

As far as we are concerned, audio cassettes like Hemi-Synch and Brother Charles work about as well as any of these machines — at least as far as getting you to a particular brain state. Admittedly, using a live, programmable, computer source allows you to custom-design an entire session, and even choose your target brain frequency to the nearest hundredth of a hertz; but not everyone needs or wants that kind of control, or that kind of expense. Further, several computer programs are emerging that allow users of multimedia-equipped computers to create their own brain machine simulations.

Chapter Nine: Thrill Of The Outdoors

Natural highs are some of the easiest ones to come by. Unfortunately, we usually associate natural scenery with nightmarish family trips or boring state park excursions. If we can rid ourselves of our conclusions about what nature has to offer consciousness, we will be free to interact with the elements that created consciousness in the first place. In nature, more than anywhere else, it is possible for us to experience how we are linked both physically and spiritually to everything else. The euphoria associated with this realization is a "natural high."

Your level of interaction with nature depends on you. You can drive for an hour in your car and look out over a vista, or you can fly to the Himalayas for a two-month camping trip. The depth of your experience of the sublime does not depend on how long, or how intensely, you are prepared to "rough it." Rather, it depends on your sensitivity to your environment and the flexibility of your state of mind. It took our businessman friend three full days staring at rocks in the middle of Utah before he could let go of his Los Angeles reality. Ever since, all he needs is a good half hour of uninterrupted time in nature to get to the same state of consciousness.

Why we get high in nature is unimportant here. It probably has something to do with the fact that for tens of thousands of years human beings lived in natural settings. We do have a natural habitat. Returning to nature gives us a sense of well being because it resonates with something deep inside us. We know that the ego and mind depend on the illusion of individuality for their survival. It is quite easy to see yourself as separate from everything else when your environment is made of inorganic materials and man-made surfaces. When you are in nature, however, you become one with your surroundings. Surfaces are porous and interactive. And while the boundary between what you call "self" and "other" gets hazy, your experience of life begins to get much clearer. Your senses improve as they delight in their interaction with their environment. (Smelling, for example, is easier when the air is sweet.) Rather than resisting life you begin to enjoy it. You approach bliss. John Denver seems to have been right.

Travel

Most of us already know something about travel. The trick to traveling for consciousness' sake is to do it for that purpose alone. Do not go sightseeing, souvenir buying or relative visiting. Do not try to "make time." Let go of "civilized" reality and immerse yourself as fully as you can in nature. There are a number of good travel agents and wilderness groups catering to people who seek spiritual travel experiences. Many are advertised in New Age magazines. Some to try are:

Above the Clouds Trekking
1-800-233-4499
PO Box 398
Worcester, MA 01602
International tours

The Great Round Vision Quests
1-707-874-2736
PO Box 201
Bodega, CA 94922
U.S. Trips

Mountain Travel
1-415-527-8100
1398 Solano Ave.
Albany, CA 94706
Domestic and International

Odyssey Tours
1-213-453-1042
1821 Wilshire Blvd.
Santa Monica, CA 90403
Asia

Off The Beaten Path
1-406-586-1311
109 E. Main St.
Bozeman, MT 59715
Rocky Mountains

Power Places Tours
1-714-497-5138
28802 Alta Laguna Blvd.
Laguna Beach, CA 92651
Domestic and International

If you have no money to travel, there are groups (other than the Peace Corps) which allow you to volunteer some services in exchange for camping or travel expenses. The best is The American Hiking Society, 1-703-385-3253, in Washington, DC. They can even let you know about opportunities for fire-watching, where you live alone in the middle of a state park in a lookout up on stilts. Your job is to stare out and watch for forest fires.

Probably the best way to get altered by traveling is to do it by yourself, or with a chosen partner, and to have as unplanned an itinerary as possible. The trip should feel as open ended as possible. The easiest thing to do is take a couple of weeks off from work, get a tent and some sleeping bags, hop in the car and drive. Just go. Take a map if you want. You don't have to camp out. You can stay in motels, or sleep in the car (where it's still legal). Take long walks on nature trails. Lose track of the time of day and the day of the week. The best of these trips are easy going, relatively risk-free excursions that keep you relaxed and open. There are also other ways.

Survival Highs

There is a high to feeling keenly aware of your own ability to survive. There are many wilderness courses (some are available through the above mentioned groups) that teach you how to survive in nature with no food, and few provisions. There is a lot to be said for these kinds of experiences. First, most of us believe we are incapable of learning how to live off the land. Gaining an ability as tangible as this directly contradicts our self-images of disconnectedness and in-eptitude. This is why so many drug rehabilitation and behavior modi-fication groups include outdoor wilderness trips in their programs.

The more completely you interact with nature, the greater your experience of oneness with it. The ability to survive in nature depends on your ability to live harmoniously with it. Western civilization generally paves over nature in order to expand. Real survival skills have nothing to do with taming nature. They allow you to perceive the way nature is moving, and to stay alive by positioning yourself properly within that movement. You become part of the organization of the woods around you.

Climbs

Another way to experience the survival high is through sports like mountain and rock climbing. While there is a level of danger in most climbing, this threat of injury or death is not the source of the high. Most good climbers do not challenge themselves beyond their abilities. They do not find this fun. If there is a "danger thrill" to climbing, it lies in the knowledge that what would have, at one time, been dangerous to undertake is now safe. The climber delights in his control over his body weight, and his ability to manipulate it up an incline.

Climbing is also a heady sport. You need to plan a particular path up a face, yet must be flexible enough to deviate from that plan as new information presents itself. As you move up a face, you approach the same consciousness of any zen-like practice, where complete mindfulness is required, coupled with effortless execution. While you do have safety equipment and partners to catch you in those moments when your zen-skills wear thin, the risks and height still command a great deal of respect, and tend to up the level of stakes for even the most veteran climbers.

Befriending the Elements

There is a beautiful book called *The Findhorn Garden*, (Harper and Row, 1975) which tells the apparently true story of how a group of people used the advice of devas to create a farm on essentially infertile soil. Their experience demonstrates the necessity for co-operation with nature and openness to the intelligences that can help us gain awareness: "We have not only to cooperate with the nature kingdoms, but we have to allow them to become one with us. Through this marriage, we are more truly human." If, after reading *The Findhorn Garden*, you want to get involved in this particular path, you can contact Peter Caddy, who is one of the founders of the Find-horn Community, through Wilson and Lake International, 1 Appian Way, #704-8, South San Francisco, CA 94080 (415-589-0352). He conducts tours of Findhorn, and arranges for people to join the Find-horn community for various lengths of time.

Of course, you can always begin on your own. There are many books available on organic gardening, so you do not have to re-invent the wheel. Luckily, there are even plans for creating a garden large enough to feed yourself, with an area only as big as a large terrace or section of rooftop, so don't worry if you live in an apartment.

Culture As Nature

Traveling to a place that is completely foreign to you, even if it is completely "civilized," can get you into some very new head spaces. The technique we are describing here is a sort of "familiarity deprivation." All you do is travel to a place where you do not speak the language or understand any of the customs. Amazing things begin to happen to you.

Your view of humanity changes. There are many things you associate with personhood that are not necessarily linked with being human. These are aspects of social behavior that your society might take for granted, but another might ignore completely. To feel the effect of this contrast, you must resist all forms of tourist advice, English media and familiar settings. There is no point in going to Jakarta and then watching CNN and eating at McDonalds. (Although there is a strange kind of high to be derived from something like that as well.)

For most of us, an extended trip abroad is necessary for the kind of radical mind shift we seek from travel. The best places to try are usually in the Far East, Indonesia or Africa, although some New Yorkers experience this kind of culture shock simply by traveling to Los Angeles for a weekend.

Chapter Ten:
From The Outside In

There is a large physical component to getting high. In fact, many of us only know that we are high when we feel physically different. It is as if our sensory functions need to be altered in order to confirm that we are experiencing a "real" change. While it is true that changes in mind and spirit can have external repercussions, the physical body, when manipulated willfully, can also alter the experience of the consciousness it houses. Getting high is a two-way street.

There are many physical therapies which act on the mind through the body. The neural pathways connecting muscle and skin to the brain provide a therapist access to your consciousness. Thus, a good massage can put your brain into alpha or delta state. A qualified doctor of acupuncture can alter the flow of life energy, chi, in your body, thus changing your experience of life itself. Similarly, you can alter your perceptions of reality by altering your body's sensations. In addition to being therapeutic, spas, hot springs, saunas and even home hot and cold water-dunks serve to break through blocked neural pathways, and provide access to new kinds of experience.

In this chapter, we'll briefly outline the theory and practice of a few of the physical therapies that alter consciousness, then describe a few things you can do to yourself.

Acupressure And Acupuncture

These are two of the main branches of oriental medicine. Just as many of the greatest mind-altering substances came out of Western pharmacological research, the several-thousand-year history of oriental medicine is not without its own nooks and crannies. Oriental medicine works by regulating chi in the body. Unlike allopathic (most Western) medicine, which battles "enemy" diseases to restore health, Eastern doctors see illness as an imbalance of energy. The systems of acupuncture and acupressure restore the chi to its proper level and circulation. Not being high can be seen as an imbalance. Either your energy level is high but misdirected and blocked, or your energy is just not high enough in the first place.

Both of these conditions can be alleviated through the practice of oriental medicine. To locate blocks, the practitioner takes something similar to pulses from the main meridian lines of the body. One meridian is associated with the liver, another with the heart, and so on. If a pulse feels a certain way, it means the meridian is blocked somewhere. To eliminate the blockages of the flow of chi, the doctor stimulates the meridian at a different point with a needle or fingers, sending energy to the point of blockage until it is cleared. If there is simply not enough energy on a particular meridian, the doctor may perform something called moxibustion, in which a herbal "moxi" stick is burned directly over an acupuncture point. The kind of heat that the moxi stick generates heats up and energizes the weak meridian.

To get high from acupuncture or acupressure requires that you not be sick when you visit the practitioner. You must go when you already feel pretty good. When the doctor asks why you have come, tell him you want more energy, or want to learn to relax better, depending upon your current state. You could also simply explain that you are visiting him for your general well being, and a balancing of your chi energies. The doctor will take pulses from different points on your wrist, determine the energy flow in each of your meridians, and then bring you into a treatment room. You will lie on a table, and the doctor will either use needles or finger pressure to stimulate certain points along the meridians that need balancing. Getting "high" off this can be felt as a subtle change or as an obvious one, depending on how aggressively the therapist chooses to work. In any case, ask what is being done to you, so that you can try to visualize the effects. If you are told that a certain acupuncture point in your foot relates to your liver, for example, try to imagine the meridian along which the chi is supposed to be traveling. The "high" of acupuncture and acupressure is a result of the rebalancing of the chi in your body. While intensely relaxing, the experience is also mind-altering. You feel as though your whole body were being adjusted to one frequency. Instead of having many disconnected parts, all doing their own thing, your mind, body and spirit become relaxed and united.

This state of being is much more energetic than it seems. As one learns in the chi-related martial arts, the best defense is to stay completely receptive. Similarly, the state of highest potential energy is a very relaxed one. When the session is over, do not run out, eat a big lunch and get caught in traffic. Don't smoke a cigarette or drink a cup of coffee. Just relax, maybe walk around outside, and look at nature. You will find you see the world differently. You may even feel disoriented. The potential difference (voltage) between different parts of your organism has been evened out. Places your energy has been unnecessarily held are now open. Most importantly, the connection between your brain/consciousness and your energy fields has been redefined. You are now free to experience life free of many barriers you were holding onto unconsciously. You may feel more relaxed, but you are actually much more alive.

Massage

Ideally, you have already experienced a good massage at some point in your life. If you have not, you are missing something extraordinary. In finding a masseuse or masseur, look for someone with some New Age or healing experience. We would be the last ones to advocate the "New Age" marketing blitz, but this is usually the best channel to find people who do body work related to consciousness expansion. If possible, meet your prospective masseuse or masseur ahead of time. Use your intuition. If you like the person, great. If you feel at all funny about him or her, find another. This person will be in intimate contact with you. If you think he or she's a creep, you won't benefit a drop.

A massage is a wonderful way of telling yourself you deserve pleasure. Most of us feel so unworthy that we deny ourselves pleasure for pleasure's sake. We have sex because we are "in a relationship." We go to therapists because it is "healthy." Get a massage because it feels great. Worry about nothing. Accept the gift of another human being's hands. Pay for it. Treat yourself. A massage is time for you to relax and someone else to work. Realizing this is half the high.

Depending upon you and the particular massage you get, you can move into any number of states of consciousness — even alpha and delta states. We have friends who have gone "out of body" during massages. Do not worry about what you are experiencing. Just relax. Many people are afraid of getting sexually aroused during a massage. Give in to whatever feeling arises, and it will probably pass. Suppressing it will only make it worse. Worst case, the masseuse or masseur sees you have an erection, or hears you moan. Big deal. They have seen it all before. You may want to laugh, cry, or scream. Cut loose. You will be told if you do something "wrong."

The beginning of a massage is the only difficult part. You will feel the spots where you are holding both physical and emotional tension. But once you begin to let go, everything will let go. Your only job is to lie there and relax. Usually what happens after the initial "letting go" phase is like sleep, but deeper. You begin to worry that you are no longer conscious of what the masseuse or masseur is doing, and that you are thus not "getting your money's worth." This is ridiculous, and will soon pass. Let the practitioner worry about your body, and let your mind float free. Massage gets you high because your body is in someone else's hands. You are being cared for. You are safe.

After a massage, follow the same rules as for acupuncture. The state of consciousness is different. You will probably feel more loving and huggy, and want to be around people rather than alone in nature. Try taking a warm shower or whirlpool, or just take a nice nap.

Rolfing

Rolfing is an extreme form of massage. People say it hurts, but it really does not have to, nor should it. Rolfing is based on a technique developed by Ida Rolf in the 1950s. Rolf's methods of massage seek to rebalance the muscle and tissue throughout the body by direct manipulation. The muscles have become unbalanced because of the shocks, injuries and upsets we have experienced through our lives. For example, if you were hit for doing something wrong when you were a child, you might still be carrying the stress of that event in the memory of your muscles. As a result, you are still holding onto that memory in your mind and body.

A good Rolfer relaxes your surface muscles enough to manipulate the deepest ones in your body. The Rolfer can break up calcium deposits, and restretch muscles to their natural state. This takes ten one-hour sessions, and is supposed to be permanent. Be careful picking your Rolfer. Certification and a good recommendation are a must. This is a very deep form of body work, and there are many people out there claiming to be Rolfers who are not.

Rolfing gets you high for a pretty obvious reason. In addition to being a form of massage, Rolfing relieves you of physical and emotional hang-ups. If you can let go of an injury, guilt, pain or grudge that has taken hold in your body for years, imagine how much lighter you will feel. Your entire relationship to gravity changes as you re-enter life with a clean slate. During the sessions, you may relive the events that led to your stress in the first place, and this may not be pleasurable. But getting truly and fully high is not always a pleasurable process. The results are what we are after.

Ida Rolf was an inspired woman. She understood the relationship of the mind to the body, and of both to the rest of reality. Her way of thinking is accessible to us in *Ida Rolf Talks About Rolfing And Physical Reality* (Rosemary Feitis, Boulder: Rolf Institute, 1978).

102

Unfortunately, many people who practice Rolfing are not as inspired as Rolf herself. They seem to think of their work as an invasive re-training of the body, rather than simply allowing the body to move into the place it really wants to be anyway. To find a good Rolfer, we recommend contacting the Rolf Institute directly: at Box 1868, Boulder, CO 80306.

Dunks

If you still do not believe that altered states are easy to attain without the use of chemicals, try this. It works best at a spa, hot spring or health club, but can even be rigged up at home. It is not advised for anyone with any ill health, or potential for ill health. People get heart attacks in saunas all the time, and that's without tempting fate like this. Patrick did not invent this technique, but he has certainly worked hard on perfecting it over the past 25 years. The sauna was the first place Patrick ever got high. He was six years old when his father first brought him into the sauna with him. It had been cold outside (Pat's from Minnesota), so the change in temperature was extreme. Young Patrick got stoned out of his little mind.

It was not until Pat's college years that he began developing the technique of getting high through extreme temperature changes. The final equation went something like this: Pat and his buddies went to a lake house in the middle of the winter. They would cut a hole in the two feet of ice covering the lake. Then, they would go indoors and heat up the sauna as hot as they could. (They managed to get it up to 220º F.) They sat in the heat until it was unbearable, then ran outside, nude, and jumped into the hole in the ice, holding on for dear life (the undercurrents were strong). Just before their bodies became too numb, they pulled themselves out of the water, and went back into the sauna. They repeated the process several times. They always ended with the cold part of the cycle, then went inside, utterly stoned.

While this method is certainly much too dangerous to be advis-able, there are many ways to achieve its effect. Go to your local sauna, hot springs or steam bath. The easiest way to try it is like this: take a shower, then go into the sauna. Usually there are tiered benches. Go to the highest one (heat rises, so it is hotter the higher you go). Sit until you feel your body is about as hot as it can get. Do not use steam yet. Let your body sweat. Once you are drenched, you are ready. Get as quickly as possible to a cold dunk. Most spas have one of these. If yours does not, go into the coldest swimming pool they have. If need be, run into a cold shower. Do not ease yourself into the cold. Go in all at once. The shock is part of the technique. The amount of time between the hot and cold phases must be very short.

As soon as you get into the water, take a breath and get your head underneath. Your whole body should be submerged. Come out for air. Try doing a "dead-man's float." Relax completely, and listen to the sounds of your body. Stay in the cold water until you are shivering, then go back into the sauna. Repeat this three times. You will be stoned, but incredibly clear at the same time. Your vision will seem improved — everything will look brighter.

You can do this at home if you have two bathrooms. Prepare one bathtub by filling it with cold water and lots of ice. (Go to the store and get some bags of ice.) Once the tub is prepared, go into a different bathroom and get in the shower. Make it as hot as you can stand without making your skin turn red. Do not scald yourself. Stay in the hot shower until your body and blood are about as hot as they are going to get. Then get out of the shower and into the cold tub as fast as you can without running. Dunk completely into the tub. This should not be done slowly. Hold your breath under the water, or lie in the tub with your mouth exposed to the air. Relax as much as possible. Once you are "too" cold, go back to the hot shower and repeat.

Always begin with hot and end with cold. Our experience of this technique is that it works through contrast. Any time you experience an extreme change, you have the opportunity to get high. Many other techniques in this book (culture shock, deprivations, hyperventilation) all exploit the fact that the consciousness is freed when the mind is disoriented. Temperature is an easily modifiable variable, and thus an ideal one to use for consciousness exploration. Note once again that you should only try a technique like this with the express permission of a medical professional.

Spas And Hot Springs

If you are serious about getting to the mind through the body, you should treat yourself to several days at a good spa. New spas are opening all the time, and provide a fairly inexpensive but totally consuming vacation experience. They range from about $500 to $2000 per week for full use of the facilities. (You can find spas for more if you look hard enough, but chances are their facilities are no better — except for the decor.) Special treatments and therapies are usually extra. A great sourcebook for finding a good spa is Ed and Judy Colbert's *The Spa Guide* (Chester, CT: The Globe Pequot Press, 1988). They list the best spas and health resorts in North America and the Caribbean. They even list cruise ships that offer spa facilities. The most important recommendation the Colberts make is to prepare for your spa visit by eating and living a little healthier before you get to the spa. This way, you will not have to go through any withdrawal while you are on vacation.

The best spas to try are ones that are built at natural hot springs and hot pools. Water heated geothermally is rich with minerals that are good for you, and tend to help the water work on you more effectively. Most natural spas also boast a large variety of therapies that healthy people can use to expand their consciousness. These include herbal wraps, hydro (water) therapies, thalusso therapy (sea water therapy), mud baths, all kinds of massage, yoga, and exercise. Spas are a "back to nature" trip, but a luxurious way to do it. Always feel free to take part in exactly how much you want to. Many spas have a regimented atmosphere. They are for unhealthy, overweight people who want to be told what to do. Try, instead, to find a spa that lets you choose how little or how much you wish to take part in.

As with any physical inroad to the psyche, you are the boss. It is your body. The key is to relax, and let your body serve you the way it was meant to.

Chapter Eleven:
Thinking Makes It So:
Head Trips

While scoffed at by nature lovers, body people, and even some gurus, the path of the intellect can be a very rewarding mind-altering experience. In addition, it usually leaves you feeling smarter, or at least having something to talk about. The great intellects of all ages invariably circulated among contemporary writers, artists, occultists and bohemians. These sages all had one thing in common: they got off on what they did.

The reason the intellect can get you high, is that it brings you closer to understanding higher truths. Contemplating the possibility of time travel, for example, forces the thinker to grapple with the notion of time itself. Pondering Jung's theory of the collective unconscious can lead to insights about thought, the interconnectedness of all living things, or even reincarnation. The intellect is an avenue towards experiencing the great trends of the cosmos.

In fact, contemplating *anything* will eventually lead you to bigger questions. One can contemplate computers, for example. The machines "think" in a binary, digital code. Everything is 1/0 or yes/no. Is that the way the whole universe is? The yin/yang? Is that what they meant? You see our point. What allows the great contemplators to think through to states of altered consciousness is their ability to mentally ramble, unedited and unashamed, through the deepest regions of their minds.

The joy of contemplation often comes from seeing how a tidbit can be generalized to explain something huge. The players of Herman Hesse's "Glass Bead Game" (in *Magister Ludi*) had a new, universal language which allowed them to ponder any branch of thought, and relate it empirically to any other. They would develop a theme from the rules of one system, and understand how they apply to another. The famous mathematician, Paul Erdos believes mathematics is not an abstraction, but an existing world that the human mind actively explores. When someone comes up with a powerful new property or formula, like Einstein's $E=mc^2$, Erdos exclaims, "that's in the book." What he means is that there are a few organizing principles in the world. Through a specific inquiry, one can reach conclusions of epic proportions. But even more importantly, in light of this book's purpose, the intellect can bring your consciousness to unexplored regions.

There is a famous story about the time James Joyce brought his daughter to see Carl Jung. Joyce was worried because she was depressed, heard voices, and lived in a fictional world. After examining her, Jung sorrowfully informed Joyce that the girl was, indeed, schizophrenic and would require a great deal of psychiatric care. Joyce became very worried. Not just for his daughter, but for himself as well. The things the daughter heard and saw were the same images Joyce contemplated, experienced and wrote about. Was he crazy too? No, replied Jung. While Joyce and his daughter were both swimming in the same deep part of the unconscious sea, Joyce was diving in, finding pearls, and returning to the surface. His daughter was drowning down there.

We mention this story not to frighten, but to inspire. The intellect does provide access to the hidden regions — the places you go to during a mystical experience. The intellect serves as fuel for a number of different vehicles that can get you high. Try any of these, or just sit with a good, smart friend and start talking.

The Tradition of Paradox

"What is the sound of one hand clapping?" calls to mind the blind old monk on *Kung Fu* who would puzzle little "Grasshopper" for ten years with this kind of question. Most religious orders have volumes of literature devoted to explanations of, and answers to, riddles that their great masters and teachers left for them. Monks often spent their days pondering a single word choice by Buddha, Krishna or Jesus.

Often, however, these questions were never meant to be answered. It was by studying the riddle, and moving your mind in the shapes and contortions that a particular riddle produces that you were to find enlightenment. In this same manner, we can re-examine the Zen koans, Sufi paradoxes, and Kabbalistic puzzles in order to reach higher states of consciousness through the intellect.

Zen Koans

The Zen koans are supposed to be unsolvable without an alteration in consciousness. To understand the question, you must move out of normal consciousness. The insight associated with solving the koan is not intellectual, but rather from outside the cerebral dimension. You ponder a koan such as "What was your face before you were born?" (from Daniel Goleman, *The Meditative Mind*, Tarcher: 1977). Whatever you are doing, you ponder this question. It is the mantra of your meditations, meals and work. The frustration becomes unbearable, until eventually your mind comes into another dimension in order to solve the problem. In the words of thirteenth century Lin-chi master Chung-feng Ming-pen:

> This principle accords with the spiritual source, tallies with the mysterious meaning, destroys birth-and-death, and transcends the passions. It cannot be understood by logic; it cannot be transmitted in words; it cannot be explained in writing; it cannot be measured by reason. It is like the poisoned drum that kills all who hear it, or like a great fire

that consumes all who come near it. ...The koan is a torch of wisdom that lights up the darkness of feeling and discrimination....For the essentials of complete transcendence, final emancipation, total penetration and identical attainment, nothing can surpass the koan. (Miura and Sasaki, pp. 5-7)

With this illumination comes a lightness of being as you understand the applications of koan to other aspects of life. The following book from which the preceding quote was taken, is an excellent source of these kinds of puzzles: *The Zen Koan* by Isshu Miura and Ruth Fuller Sasaki (Harvest/HBJ: 1965). Another excellent starting place is *Zen Flesh and Zen Bones* by Paul Reps (Doubleday).

If you'd like to try working on a koan, here's a sample: "A monk asked Baso: 'What is Buddha?' Baso said: 'This mind is not Buddha.'" According to Master Mu-mon, anyone who fully understands this koan is a master of Zen. Another: "Shuzan held out his short staff and said: 'If you call this a short staff, you oppose its reality. If you do not call it a short staff, you ignore the fact. Now what do you wish to call this?'" (Both of these are from Reps.)

Sufi-Teaching Stories

In a tradition similar to the Zen masters', the Sufis also engage in long contemplations of paradoxes, hoping, too, that the working out of these problems will lead to higher consciousness. Instead of posing riddles, the Sufis generally tell stories for which enlightenment is a prerequisite to understanding. These teaching stories, or dervish tales, all end in apparent non sequiturs. Finding the connection — making sense of the characters' actions or words — releases the spiritual energy that thrusts one further on the path toward enlightenment. Idries Shah, respected in the Sufi tradition, has written several volumes of teaching stories. He insists that "The inner dimensions of teaching stories, however, are held to make them capable of revealing, according to the stage of development of the student, more and more planes of significance." Our favorite of Shah's translations is called "The Cradle."

> A child was born, and the father went to a carpenter and asked him to make a cradle for it.
>
> The carpenter told him to come back in a week to collect it. When he returned it was not finished.
>
> The man went back week after week, and still the cradle was not to be seen.
>
> Eventually the child grew into a man. In his turn he married and his wife bore him a child.
>
> His own father said to him: 'Go to see the carpenter and ask him whether your cradle is ready yet.'
>
> So the young man went to the carpenter's shop and reminded him about the cradle.
>
> 'Here is an opportunity,' he said, 'for you to finish the job. I now have a small son, and the cradle will be ideal for him.'
>
> 'Be off with you!' said the carpenter: 'I refuse to be stampeded in my work just because you and your family are obsessed by what they want!' " (*The Way of the Sufi*, Idries Shah, Dutton: 1970, p. 199)

The Sufis warn against using these stories, or any practices for that matter, in order to produce highs: "The jackal thinks that he has feasted well, when he has in fact only eaten the leavings of the lion. I transmit the science of producing 'states.' This, used alone, causes damage. He who uses it only will become famous, even powerful. He will lead men to worship 'states,' until they will almost be unable to return to the Sufi Path." (Abdul-Qadir of Gilan — in Shah, p. 128)

In Sufism, as with almost any of the religious paths suggested in this chapter, the seeker must be ready to commit more than a passing fancy to the philosophies and practices. These are not highs that can be easily experienced in one afternoon of effort. The following practice is no exception.

Kabbalah

Kabbalah is said to have developed out of spiritual necessity. The Jews of this tradition believe that there was once a kind of cosmic harmony on earth, perpetuated by the proper placement of the original ten commandments in an ark in the first temple. It is said to have functioned like a crystal in a great cosmic radio. At this time in history, prophets walked the earth, and knew that invasion was imminent, and the temple would be destroyed. The Jews constructed an elaborate subterranean labyrinth for the Ark of the Covenant. Meanwhile, the prophets, knowing their time on earth was limited, created scriptures which, properly deciphered, hold the secrets of the universe, and the keys to restoring harmony on the planet. These works include the Torah and some of the later books of the Old Testament.

For reasons even they did not fully understand, the Jews passed on these scriptures, following strict rules for exactly how they were to be transcribed and pronounced. Early Jewish scholars began to slowly decipher these texts using techniques ranging from numerology, to elaborate diagrams of the order of the universe. For the dedicated intellectual, it's supposed to be pretty rewarding stuff. "Using the Psalms as a guide book for their visualizations of God's environs, these early mystics embodied ascending grades of consciousness in concrete images that eventually lost their form and merged into pure light....After passing though seven states of consciousness...the mystic traversed seven further 'heavens' before arriving at the Throne of God. The vision usually culminated here with the projected form of a cosmic man poised upon a brilliant seat of glory." (*Kabbalah: The Way of the Jewish Mystic*, Perle Epstein, Shambhala: 1978)

Unfortunately, Kabbalah just isn't the kind of path you can try out on a free afternoon. We don't have the space here to demonstrate the kinds of enlightenment potentiated by these studies, but we assure you that for Westerners especially, they are quite rewarding. Part of the thrill of Kabbalah for us is the fact that the main source of mystical energy is the Bible itself, which has been right under our noses (sometimes pushed there) since we were kids. The most obviously mystical sections are the first chapter of Genesis, and the first chapter of Ezekiel (the most magical of the prophets). The other main source of inspiration for the mystics is contemplation of the Cosmic Tree (the tree of life), an elaborate diagram for the structure of the universe, and possible levels of consciousness. For further study, first try *Kabbalah: Tradition of Hidden Knowledge* by Z'Ev ben Shimon Halevi (NY: Thomas and Hudson, 1979). It's easy to read, well diagrammed, and written by a fine teacher of Jewish mysticism. Also excellent *is Path of the Kabbalah* by David Shienkin (NY: Paragon, 1986).

Betting Systems

Being able to predict the future has obvious benefits. But the ancient systems of astrology, Tarot, the I Ching, and Runes did not develop merely as divinatory tools; they attempt to explain the nature of time and our motion through it. Studying any of these systems can lead to great spiritual insight, whether or not you care to know the wealth of your next lover.

All of these techniques locate trends and cycles in the universe. The earth seems to circle the sun every 365 ¼ days. Certain things seem to happen in certain months. The positions of planets seem to influence, or at least indicate forces at work on earth. Time seems cyclical rather than linear. These ideas are based on a holographic view of the world: the tea leaves in the bottom of your cup are part of the motion of the universe, and can thus reflect the movement of all of nature, assuming the reader has a proper method of divination. Similarly, six tosses of three I Ching coins produce one of 64 hexagrams that indicates the tosser's state of being, or answers his or her questions.

Our interest here is not necessarily in practicing these techniques, but in exploring how they were developed, and how they work. If intellectual highs are produced by momentarily understanding our connection to everything else around us, then surely the study of forms which demonstrate this fact are in order.

112

A few good sources for this kind of study are:

Astrology:
The Inner Sky by Steven Forrest, San Diego, CA: ACS Publications, 1988

The Art and Practice of Chinese Astrology, Derek Walters, NY: Simon and Schuster, 1987.

Tarot:
The Mystic Tarot (comes with a deck of cards), Juliet Sharman-Burke and Liz Greene.

Motherpeace: A Way to the Goddess through Myth, Art and Tarot.

Aleister Crowley's *The Book of Thoth*, York Beach, ME: Samuel Weiser, 1974.

A New Handbook for the Apprentice, by Eileen Connolly, North Hollywood: Newcastle, 1979.

I Ching:
The Taoist I Ching, Thomas Cleary, trans. Boston, MA: Shambhala, 1986.

The Philosophy of The I Ching, Carol K. Anthony, Stow, MA: Anthony Publishing, 1981.

Runes:
The Book of Runes, Ralph Blum, NY: Oracle Books

Not For Nerds Only:
Science And Math

Descriptive math and science — the kinds most of us learned in school — can be pretty boring. The reason we were taught these subjects with a practical orientation is obvious: what sells science to Western society is the fact that it's useful. Math can be used to calculate deficits or interest rates, while science is applied to determine how much gas a certain engine needs to go 400 miles, or how many calories are in a bowl of tapioca pudding. These are not useless facts; but the experiments or calculations involved in obtaining them rarely get you high. The transcendental quality of math and science — what interests us here — is that they attempt to make sense out of chaos. The manner in which they do so differs, however.

Math As Nirvana

Math assumes perfection. It has its own reality, and exists independently of the natural world. A certain equation will always lead to a certain graph. Newton's equations for harmonic motion (a pendulum or spring) would remain perfect on their own terms, even if something in the real world were to change. Math is correct. Much of the real world, as seemingly chaotic as it, can be explored through systems of equations. Finding the equations that explain the cosmos leads to an expansion of consciousness.

Learning math is like studying history. It is generally taught in the order it was discovered. We learn arithmetic, algebra, geometry, then trigonometry (the combination of algebra and geometry), and from trigonometry we deduce calculus. There is beauty in just learning these subjects. Assuming you aren't worried about a grade, or memorizing a theorem or identity, there is joy to be derived from finding an elegant solution to a seemingly complex equation. We hated math in school, because the focus was on being able to solve problems with memorized techniques in a short amount of time. Today, if we pick up a math text, we can read through it with pleasure. Believe us, this is true. If you don't have to memorize what you're reading, you can follow the arguments, and observe the workings of the mathematical systems in the same way you might explore the workings of an intricate Swiss watch.

Where math gets really fun, however, is when it gets in the hands of people like Ralph Abraham. This University of California at Santa Cruz math professor took a day off in 1967 to explore his consciousness. He returned seven years later. He had traveled Europe and Asia, spent months in caves, and experienced the Logos. Sitting in the dark in the mountain caves of Tibet, Abraham had striking visions of vibratory fields. Only later did he realize that these visions could be considered three-dimensional graphs of dynamic systems. Somehow, nirvana and math were related. Abraham is spending the majority of his time communicating his findings to the likes of us. He has written four picture books about the geometry of behavior, which read more like children's books than math texts, so don't be intimidated. While he knows his experience of the dynamics of behavior is probably incommunicable, he does hope that "perhaps a visual representation would excite the full field in the viewer's mind through morphic resonance." That is, because the pictures in the book are visual representations of a deep reality, they excite a recognition response in those who view and understand them. For us, this has worked, and we highly recommend Abraham's series of books: *Dynamics: The Geometry of Behavior*, Abraham and Shaw, Ariel Press (PO Box 1360, Santa Cruz, CA 95061). There are currently four volumes: *Periodic Behavior, Chaotic Behavior, Global Behavior*, and *Bifurcation Behavior*. Ariel Press also boasts a catalogue of other math texts and publications on the cutting edge of consciousness exploration.

Getting Off On The Scientific Model

Science, on the other hand, knows it is probably wrong about most everything. We've all had a science teacher in high school tell us smugly that half of what we were to learn that year would probably be wrong. The beauty of science is the evolution of the scientific model. This model, huge, clunky, and full of "exceptions," attempts to explain nature. It got its start when people wanted to know what stars were, or why fire works, and was developed by Descartes and Galileo through Newton to Einstein and now us. So if at one time atoms were believed to be the fundamental particle, it was just a matter of time before a scientist realized this could not be true, hypothesized what a subatomic particle might look like, then experimented further to test his hypothesis. Even if he was "proved" correct, it was only a matter of time before someone realized that there was a yet smaller fundamental particle. After that, the scientific model makes an even more radical change as scientists wonder if matter really exists at all, or if the fundamental particle is really just a form of energy. You get the general idea here.

At one time, the scientific model assumed Newton's laws worked for everything. All reality was explainable by the laws which govern the movement of masses on earth. Then we realized this was not the case, and have been trying to explain it ever since. Quantum physics, in a desperate attempt to save what was left of the model, proposed that Newton's laws work on earth for things of average size, but that other laws would be needed in order to explain subatomic particles and the movement of planets. It's been a free-for-all ever since, which is why it's so interesting.

The current movement in science could even be considered spiritual. Scientists have become aware of the interconnectedness of all things. In theory, at least, positrons from the same nucleus will maintain their identical direction of spin, even if separated over huge distances. If the spin of one of these positions were changed, the other one would change too, even though it is in no physical proximity. Similarly, when attempting to create new crystalline structures, scientists may work weeks or months trying to get the atoms to align in a certain way. Once they do, however, and a new crystal is created, the same crystal structure will appear spontaneously in labs throughout the world. It is as if once the atoms are "taught" to align in a certain way, all atoms of the same type somehow gain this ability too. In a strange echo of Jung's theory of a collective unconscious, the behavior of these particles, and analogous behavior of animals, is called morphic resonance. At Harvard, William McDougal taught a large population of rats how to go through a certain maze. Spontaneously and unexplainably, rats in Europe gained this knowledge too.

Places to begin this kind of exploration are *Beyond the Quantum* by Michael Talbot, *A Brief History of Time*, by Stephen Hawking, and

The Tao of Physics, by Fritjof Capra. Or go to your local university bookstore and browse the shelves, or audit courses that sound interesting. Many colleges offer courses like "Physics for Poets," or "Philosophy of Science," usually taught by scientists with a need to share their highs.

Myth And Philosophy

Much more popular with intellectual seekers these days are the paths of the seemingly less scientific thinkers. Joseph Campbell, for example, shares a sense of the "oneness" of all consciousness through his exhaustive research of nearly all the world's mythologies. In *The Power of Myth*, he even shares his concept of bliss, and how he believes all people can attain it for themselves. Rather than search these kinds of books for answers though, one should get high through the experience of understanding what is being communicated.

People like Campbell, or Alan Watts, or Aldous Huxley are all trying to communicate an experience outside of language. Poets of the intellect, these men have created works of literature that transcend language, and create the experience of "oneness" that is being high. Through the intellectual understanding of our place as part, center, and full manifestation of the universe, we reach a state of bliss.

Campbell's work has become quite popular since the series of interviews he did with Bill Moyer aired on PBS. These interviews are available on videotape at your local video store, and we recommend them as an introduction to Campbell's body of work. *The Power of Myth* (New York: Doubleday, 1988) is a compilation of these interviews, and reading it can be an interesting experience. An advocate of reaching and attaining bliss, Campbell explains how "I thought, 'I don't know whether my consciousness is proper consciousness or not; I don't know whether what I know of my being is proper or not; but I do know where my rapture is. So let me hang on to rapture, and that will bring me both my consciousness and my being.' I think it worked."

The list of brilliant thinkers goes on and on. Of particular interest might be the work of Carl Jung, a psychologist who spent his life developing the theory of the collective unconscious, and exploring the archetypal images shared by all people, of all times. Start out with a collection of Jung's essays to decide which branch of his voluminous body of work most interests you.

Alan Watts was probably one of this century's last great philosophers. His works are available in print or on cassette from Alan Watts Electronic Educational Programs, Box 938, Point Reyes Station, CA 94956 (415-663-9102). A good departure point into his mind would be his autobiography, *In My Own Way* (NY: Vintage Books, 1973) which chronicles the development of his thinking. Watts was a student of Zen who got "turned on" to psychedelics in the sixties, then became a popular philosopher with the intellectual wing of the beat generation. His description of an LSD trip in *The Joyous Cosmology* surpasses even Huxley's *Doors of Perception*. In Watts' words,

> The active and the passive are two phases of the same act. A seed, floating in its white sunburst of down, drifts across the sky, sighing with the sound of a jet plane invisible above. I catch it by one hair between thumb and index finger, and am astonished to watch this little creature actually wiggling and pulling as if it were struggling to get away. Common sense tells me that this tugging is the action of the wind, not of the thistledown. But then I recognize that it is the "intelligence" of the seed to have just such delicate antennae of silk that, in an environment of wind, it can move.... True, the seed does not intend to move itself with the wind, but neither did I intend to have arms and legs. (*The Joyous Cosmology*, NY: Vintage Books, 1965, pp. 68-69)

Also of interest are Terence and Dennis McKenna, who originally used psychedelics to develop their theory of time and consciousness. Their most interesting books are *The Invisible Landscape: Mind, Hallucinogens, and The I Ching*, and *True Hallucinations*. The

McKennas are very unorthodox thinkers, but they support all of their notions with exhaustive scientific research. While a little dense for some readers, *The Invisible Landscape* is a mind-expanding argument for the oneness and circularity of our existence:

> The unformed archetypes of the collective unconscious may be the holographic substrate of the species' mind. Each individual mind-brain is then like a fragment of the total hologram; but, in accordance with holographic principles, each fragment contains the whole. It will be remembered that each part of a hologram can reconstruct an entire image, but that the details of the image will deteriorate in proportion to its fragmentation, while the overstructure will remain. Out of this feature of holography arises the quality of individual point of view and, in fact, individuality itself. If each mind is a holographic medium, then each is contiguous with every other, because of the ubiquitous distribution of information in a hologram. Each individual mind would thus be a representation of the "essence" of reality, but the details could not be resolved until the fragments of the collective hologram were joined. (*The Invisible Landscape*, p.47)

Easier access to the McKenna minds is in a "talking book" (cassette tapes) called *True Hallucinations* available through Sound Photosynthesis, PO Box 2111, Mill Valley, CA 94942. They also carry the audio works of philosophers including Robert Anton Wilson, Timothy Leary, John Lilly, and William Burroughs.

Easier to understand, but still somewhat transcendental are books by Joseph Chilton Pearce. *The Crack in the Cosmic Egg* is a good first step in the exploration of philosophy as an intellectual path towards bliss.

This seems like the best place to mention one of our favorite philosophical books. It's a fairly optimistic and very convincing argument for the imminent radical evolution of the human species to a higher form of consciousness. *Unknown Man* by Yatri (NY: Simon and Schuster, 1988) is a beautifully illustrated volume that encompasses everything from schizophrenia to Buddhafield, while maintaining the tone of a good after dinner discussion. Reading the book, and accepting the fact that someday soon we may all be high, all the time, is mind-altering in itself.

Read Any Good Books Lately?

Lastly, fiction provides immediate access to the thought processes of transcendental thinkers. The rule of thumb is to find authors who have had mystical experiences, and then read the works that immediately followed those events. These kinds of texts have been written for centuries.

Ancient works include the Tibetan and Egyptian Books of the Dead, which detail the experiences a soul goes through after its host body dies. The purpose of these books is not only to prepare you for death, but to imitate the experience of death so that you can be "reborn" into your own lifetime. Medieval Europe had its share of mystics too. Especially interesting are the writings of the anchoress mystics like Julian of Norwich, who usually wrote their greatest works after experiencing a prolonged fever or near-death experience.

More up-to-date literary simulations of the mystical experience come from authors like James Joyce, Herman Hesse, Aldous Huxley or poets like Yeats or T.S. Eliot. Understanding Joyce's *Finnegan's Wake*, it is said, is as impossible as understanding the cosmos. The story is a dream, and the images used to describe that dream are taken from everywhere in literature. No one could possibly identify even a majority of the references and puns. But, as Joyce would have us believe, all of the information we need to decipher the text is accessible to us in the collective, cultural unconscious. And, indeed, you will experience moments reading Joyce's masterpiece when your attempts at understanding the words disappear, and your consciousness resonates in full comprehension somewhere between yourself and the text. It is believed that the following passage is about two washerwomen at the shores of an expanding river, finding themselves becoming immobile parts of the landscape as the river

120

widens. Try reading aloud and it might just make sense. A phrase like "My foos won't moos" might mean to say "my foot won't move," while also communicating that moss is growing.

> Can't hear with the waters of.
> The chittering waters of. Flittering bats,
> fieldmice bawk talk. Ho! Are you not gone a
> home? What Thom Malone? Can't hear
> with bawk of bats, all thim lifeying waters of.
> Ho, talk save us! My foos won't moos. I
> feel as old as yonder elm. A tale told of
> Shaun or Shem? All Livia's daughtersons.
> Dark hawks hear us. Night! Night! My ho
> head halls. I feel as heavy as yonder stone.
> Tell me of John or Shaun? Who were Shem and
> Shaun the living sons or daughters of? Night
> Now! Tell me, tell me, tell me, elm! Night
> night! Telmetale of stem or stone. Beside
> the rivering waters of, hitherandthithering
> waters of. Night!
> (*Finnegan's Wake* in Norton Anthology, p. 2139.)

Chapter Twelve:
Eyes Closed:
Sleep, Dreams And Journeys

While getting high and walking around in that state of consciousness is a wonderful thing, there are several ways to alter yourself that involve sleep and fantasy. These are inward journeys, where instead of looking at familiar things differently, you take your waking consciousness to unfamiliar regions. If the mountain will not come to Mohammed...

The trick with any of the techniques in this chapter is to stay conscious. Most of us have probably had lucid dreams, experiential visualizations, and even out-of-body experiences, but have not remembered them. You cannot really consider them highs if you experienced them while you were asleep, and then woke up with no memory that they ever happened. The technique to develop is to be able to watch what you are doing. You become two people at once: a participant and an observer. If you are in a dream, you want to be able to behave consciously. If you are in a dream being chased by bad guys, and you know you are having a dream, you can jump out the window and fly away. Or you can decide to grow six more feet and beat them up. Similarly, if you can follow yourself consciously as you move into an out-of-body experience, you can learn to direct your travels, and go anywhere you wish.

The techniques in this chapter, then, are not "highs." They do not change your waking state of consciousness. Rather, they allow you to move your consciousness into new regions. Once there, you are open to an immense range of possible actions, feelings, and landscapes. You are free to travel into different dimensions of reality. Instead of altering your mind to see the everyday world differently, you leave the mind alone, and go into different space.

Lucid Dreaming

The sleep state is the most accessible of the altered states. We get there almost every night of our lives. Still, to most of us, the eight or so hours we spend in bed are like wasted time. We awake refreshed, but remember almost nothing. It is relatively easy to gain conscious access to the sleep state. There are a number of books and tapes designed to help you to remember your dreams, and then to behave consciously within them. Most of these methods, with a little discipline on your part, work.

The foremost expert in the field of lucid dreaming is Stephen LaBerge. To do any dream work before reading his *Lucid Dreams* (Los Angeles: Tarcher Inc., 1985) would be inefficient. He has mapped it all out already. Tapes are also available that help you to remember and take part in your dreams. The ones that worked best for us were the subliminal tapes called *Lucid Dreaming: Awaken to Your Inner Self*, put out by Yes! Technologies, 16 Finalee Ave., Asheville, NC 28803. The tapes are not a necessary component here, but, if nothing else, they heighten your awareness as you are going to sleep that you have a purpose in mind.

The tapes are part of a simple program which gives the subliminal suggestion that when you hear a certain sound, you will spontaneously begin to dream lucidly. You play the suggestion tapes during the day. Then at night, you play a special tape on an auto-reverse cassette deck. This technique worked in about a week, but we found we had little control over our own actions in our dreams. We were conscious that we were dreaming, but not free to move around. Still, the dreams we had were amazingly vivid, if not altogether lucid. (We realize this last comment raises a myriad of questions about dream morality. For example, should we even try to have control over our dreams? Aren't they an expression of our subconscious which should be left alone? Maybe. But to us, the fun of lucid dreaming is to get to play inside our fantasies. We can still have other dreams for our subconscious' sake.)

The first step in learning to have lucid dreams on your own is to start remembering your dreams. The way to do this is to choose to do so. Before you go to sleep, tell yourself you are going to remember your dreams. Keep a pad next to your bed, and whenever you wake up, discipline yourself to write down whatever you have been dreaming. If you just cannot remember, at least write down how you feel — this might allow you to recall the source of those feelings.

Once you have a fairly good recall of your evening's dreams, you can begin the process of moving into them consciously. We have done this in two ways. Both of them involve recognizing the fact that you are dreaming without waking up. This in between place is the lucid dream. They say lucid dreams occur most often in morning REM (rapid eye movement) sleep. The method of exploiting morning sleep time is simple. When you first wake up, actively remember what you just dreamed. Go through the location and characters in your mind until you know the world of the dream very well. Then, go back to sleep, telling yourself that when you see this world again, you will know it is a dream. Do it the same way you remind yourself that the moment you start to make the coffee in the morning, you will remember that you have to make a certain phone call. You may not re-enter into the same exact dream, but chances are you will recognize it as a dream. Do this and experiment until you can play inside your dreams. If you take too extreme of an action — one that does not fit in the world of the dream — you might tend to wake yourself up. You must learn how to maintain the dream state without breaking it up.

Another way of entering your dreams consciously is to work at it as you go to sleep. This is the way that has worked best for our friend Benjamin. As he enters the state between waking and sleeping, he begins to imagine walking or moving. As a child, Ben used to imagine running down the aisles of a huge toy store, and watching all the items pass by in his peripheral vision. He would keep running until it did not even feel like he was running anymore, but was instead gliding, or even flying. The wall of the toy store would open in front of him, and he would fly through all sorts of tunnels, skies, and canyons. If he could keep conscious through all this, he would end up having marvelously lucid dreams.

Anyone can imitate this process by consciously fantasizing during the falling asleep time. As you let go more and more, you get closer and closer to the dream state. Just hold onto one of your senses consciously — like sight — and you will have a conscious window into your dream. The problem is, you tend to fall into sleep after the dream and then forget the whole thing. There are easy ways to combat this problem. Try setting a gentle alarm (the music option on a clock radio) to go off maybe ten minutes into the process. If you have a snooze bar, this should keep you waking up every ten minutes. Better yet, have a partner hit the snooze bar for you so you do not even have to move. The music will gently remind you not to fall completely into sleep. After three or four of these cycles, wake up and record your experience. This same process would work better for many people at the prime "launch window" hours of early morning.

You should keep a good journal of your dream experiences. This is one of the only ways to get better at dreaming — that is, to get deeper and deeper access through the dreaming state of consciousness. Through dreams, we can communicate with parts of ourselves, and perhaps with other people and entities altogether. But the only way to travel down this road is by documenting and mapping out where we have gone already. By recognizing patterns in our dreams over, say a two-year period, we can get a much better sense of where we are going, and how to get there more efficiently. A good sourcebook on how to get the most out of your dreams is Strephon Kaplan-Williams' *The Jungian-Senoi Dreamwork Manual* (Berkeley, CA: Journey Press, 1980 — available through Journey Press, PO Box 9036, Berkeley, CA, 94709). This workbook outlines everything you ever wanted to know about dreaming but were afraid to ask. The author goes into little detail on lucid dreaming itself, but his comments on how to interpret your dream symbols, as well as how to approach your dreams openly, yet systematically, are indispensable to the purposeful dreamer.

When you work the *Manual,* you realize that every dream is a trip outside of the time-space continuum. Dreams have the same shape as sex, acid trips, or a near-death experience. You "die" into the dream, and are reborn out of it, able to live your life as a new person. Each night of your life can be the most intense experience you have ever passed through, and you will still get a good night's sleep.

Visualization

Visualizations can be used for many purposes. Their most dramatic function has been to aid in the healing of cancer victims, who visualize the cells of their own body fighting and destroying cancer cells. People like Dr. Bernie Siegal (*Love, Medicine, Miracles,* NY: Harper and Row, 1986) have written on the ability of people to self-heal through creative imagery. Most common are visualizations that help people relax. Even if they cannot heal themselves directly, they can at least break the cycle of being sick, getting tense, and becoming sicker. Our interest in visualizations, though, is how to use them to reach noticeably new states of consciousness.

While it is important to remove the connotations of visualization as exclusively a healing technique, it is also important to distinguish between visualizations and affirmations. Affirmations are a way of trying to make something true that either is not true, or that you cannot see as true. Someone who is experiencing his life as impoverished, for example, might tell himself an affirmation every morning of: "I have all the money I need. I am a magnet for money." They may also "visualize" themselves as very rich, or driving an expensive car, or living in a mansion. Eventually, the image the person imagines and reality are supposed to meet. We do not think this is the case. Every time you repeat an affirmation to yourself, such as "I am a beautiful person," you are actually communicating the opposite. What you really hear and feel is, "I need to tell myself I am a beautiful person, because I am not." The affirmation is something outside of yourself that is supposed to feed your self-image. This is impossible. All it does is accentuate the difference between where you are and where you want to be. If you want to do visualizations of this kind, the best book is Shakti Gawain's *Creative Visualization* (NY: Bantam Books, 1982). Many people feel they have benefited from this work; it has nothing to do with getting high.

Being high depends on you being exactly how and where you want to be at a given moment. Getting high means getting free of time-space. When you are high, you do not need to remind yourself of anything. Visualizations that get you high work by releasing the mind. They become like dreams, where the rules of reality no longer hold. They may bring you deeper into the workings of your body, or even bring you out of your body altogether.

Visualizations are really just organized, sometimes preplanned fantasies. A person will lie down, close his eyes, and then listen to a tape or person guide him through an imagined experience. Therapists use them to help patients get over problems by accessing their subconscious creativity. The subconscious is allowed to communicate with the conscious. For example, a therapist might say, "You find an envelope. Inside the envelope is a note. Who is the note from?" The patient may answer, "It's from my father." The therapist responds, "Read the note..." You get the idea. It is a directed free association.

We can direct the visualizations any way we want. We can even direct them ourselves, if we are not embarrassed to fantasize. In any case, with a little practice, we can bring ourselves, through imagery, into a desired state of consciousness. In acting, this technique is called "sense memory." To feel a certain way, an actor will remember what he was seeing, smelling, hearing, tasting, or touching during some event in his life when he felt that way. After he has accurately recalled these sensations, and concentrated on them, he will usually begin to feel the same way. By visualizing sensations we have never experienced though, we can bring our consciousness into states we have never experienced either.

The easy way to start doing visualizations is to buy prerecorded ones on tape. The first one that comes to mind for exciting head travel is a very bizarre one called *The Cauldron of Thoth* available through Nicki Scully, PO Box 5025, Eugene, OR, 97405. It has a rather pagan feeling about it, but it takes you through an out-of-body experience, as well as introducing you to some of the characters in Egyptian mythology. There's also some pretty cool music. You can find lots of less intense visualization tapes at any New Age bookstore. Just make sure not to get any tape that is for something in particular. Most of these cassettes are sold as visualizations to quit smoking or to lose weight. Just get one that says it is for a good time, or for general relaxation.

Another great source of visualizations is the *Anthology of Imagery Techniques* edited by Anees A. Sheikh, Ph.D. (Milwaukee: American Imagery Institute, 1986). This tome lists dozens of visualizations, as well as ways to use them.

The best technique for doing prepared visualizations is to record them on tape, then listen to them. Be sure to leave time for yourself to imagine whatever you are narrating. For example, if you are reciting "you come to a stone wall... you see a man sitting on top... you walk up to the man..." be sure to leave pauses during which you will be able to imagine what the wall and man look like. You can also have a friend read one to you, or take turns reading them to each other.

It helps to set up an atmosphere conducive to the energy of fantasy. Burn candles and incense, turn the lights low, and play some evocative music.

Here is an example of a visualization that can get you high:

Your body is heavy... it is one with the earth... you can feel the gravity the earth exerts on you... you can feel the gravity you exert on the earth... you are living in an open field... the sun is bright above you... but there is also a cool breeze... the air is sweet and delicious... you can feel the cool green grass beneath you... you can touch it with your hands... you look up into the sky... it is blue except for the sun directly above you...

With each breath in and out, your awareness of the planet beneath you grows... it is most definitely round... it is most definitely moving... you are on your back, in the middle of a field, on a whirling sphere... the movement is delightful... you feel the blood in your body come to the surface of your skin from the motion... enjoy the sensation...

You get curious about the world around you... you look around... there are trees at the edge of the field... you decide to get up to investigate, and the moment you make the decision you feel your body begin to rise by itself... your head rises first, followed by your body... you are completely vertical, and still rising... as you rise, you look around yourself.... see the trees... past the trees are little towns...past the towns are lakes, rivers, bridges... you rise higher and higher... you can see the curving of the earth... the circular horizon...

As you rise you begin to feel warm... you are closer to the sun... but inside you too, there is a warmth... a fire seems to be burning inside you, propelling your motion upwards like the engines of a rocket ship... you get hotter and hotter... your face becomes flush... it is a beautiful, encompassing warmth... you are heated inside and out... you rise with amazing speed...

You feel warm most of all in the center of your chest... it feels as if there were an ice cube deep in the middle of your chest being melted... as the ice cube melts, it turns to water... the water diffuses throughout your body... your whole consciousness is in this ice cube now... you feel yourself melting away into liquid... your body seems to drop away as you become just water and heat... flame and liquid, rising into the sky...

The water becomes so warm that it turns to vapor, bringing you into the air as steam... the fire drops away back to the earth, which is miles and miles below you... you are just vapor... you spread out into the air... you are one with the air... you diffuse throughout the atmosphere... you are embracing the earth as air... you feel cool and sweet as air itself... you have no weight... you have no form... you are air...

You continue to flow outward... it is no longer getting brighter... the sky is actually getting darker and cooler... the earth has become a small sphere within you as you continue to move out... you are moving out into space... you are air, diffusing into space...

You move outward in all directions at once... you move beyond air... you are lighter and lighter... smoother and smoother... you are moving into the absolute textureless dark... there is no feeling, no direction... just movement... float... enjoy...

When you want to, realize that the blackness around you is the inside of a huge body... fill the void of this huge, human body with your consciousness... fill its legs... fill its hands... fill its abdomen... fill its chest... fill its head... bring warmth and life to this new body...

Enjoy the feeling of weight... this new body is lying on the ground... lying on cool grass... look around you... you are back in the warm field... the sun is still directly above you... the cool breeze blows against your face... you are where you were.

Take time to rest before slowly opening your eyes, stretching, and sitting up.

We have found the best way to do visualizations, though, is freestyle. Just lie down in the same way, and imagine what you want to. You do not need to put it into words. Just visualize whatever kind of journey you want to take, and take it.

Out-Of-Body Travel

Out-of-body experiences are not everyday events — at least not for most of us. The first and still the foremost out-of-body adventurer in the modern scientific community is Robert A. Monroe, whose book *Journeys Out of the Body*, (NY: Anchor Press, 1971,1977) and its sequel, *Far Journeys*, (NY: Dolphin Books, 1985) are the best documentation available on the subject.

Mystics, awakened teachers and shamans go out-of-body regularly, but usually as the result of a talent they are born with. They can tell you stories about the places they have gone and the entities they have met, but cannot really share the process by which they get out of the physical body. They just do — this is why they are shamans. Occasionally, someone with a normal background has a spontaneous journey out-of-body. It could be during an intense meditation, while going to sleep, during an accident, or just during nothing special at all.

Most people react to an out-of-body experience as a fantasy. They cannot believe it really happened. It is so out of place with the physical reality, that they assume it was a hallucination, and tell no one. But Robert Monroe realized that, during the night, he was actually traveling outside of his body. He wrote his first book about these experiences, then set up The Monroe Institute of Applied Sciences to study out-of-body travel.

Since then, he has trained thousands of people to get out of their bodies for varying periods of time. The traveler lies in bed in one room, in voice contact with a monitor, who watches the vital signs of the voyager from a control console down the hall. It's like a science-fiction movie, except the results are real. Monroe developed recordings of tones at frequencies that get people into a state of consciousness where they are physically asleep, yet mentally awake. It is from this state that the person can get out-of-body.

Monroe has made these sounds available on tape. A catalog is available from the Institute, located in Faber, VA, 804-361-1500. You can get started with a set of cassettes that should run you about thirty dollars. If you intend to get out-of-body, this is the way to begin. For a more hands-on experience, you can take a week-long workshop at the Institute itself. The starter course, including room and board, should run you about one thousand dollars. From our contact with the Institute, we can honestly say they are not scammers. These people believe in what they are doing, love what they are doing, and want to share it with as many people as possible. It is not just a business, but a research center. Still, as with any organization, you should maintain your own desired distance or level of involvement.

The research they have done is amazing. They are uncovering a map of the universe that has nothing to do with the galaxies that we know about. They explore inner space — or is it true outer space? — and accurately document everything they find. They have contacted dozens of kinds of "entities," and found many, many different realms of existence. They are coming to understand everything from reincarnation to the nature of life itself. The out-of-body explorers who work at the Institute make even the most earnest channeling look like a parlor game.

Monroe outlined in his first book a way to get out-of-body, but admitted in his second book that the approach does not work for all people all the time. Getting out-of-body is not as simple as he first believed. Still, the technique has worked for many people, and even if you do not get complete satisfaction, it is probably still the best preliminary training for you to begin with.

Monroe breaks up the learning process into three major steps: relaxation, vibration, and separation. To get properly relaxed, you need to be able to recognize and exploit a sleeping body with an awake mind. You are first to practice this exercise at bedtime. Get to the place where you feel yourself dozing off, and without moving, keep your mind alert by concentrating on one thing. Stay in this state for as long as possible. Once you can do this, see if you can stay in this state without concentrating on one thing in particular. Many thoughts and impressions from the day will appear to you when you are in this state. Let them all pass until you just see black. This could take a week or so of nights.

After you can do this, attempt to get into the same state when you are not tired. This is tricky, but not impossible. Monroe suggests trying this on waking from a night's sleep, or after a nap, so that your body is still relaxed.

Monroe next talks about a vibrational state. This is as far as we have gotten with his technique so far. Monroe advises removing any and all possible distractions (telephone, roommates, etc.) and lying in a semi-dark room. You are to hold yourself in the deepest state of relaxation you can, while breathing through a half-opened mouth. Next, he says to:

> Concentrate on the blackness in front of your closed eyes. Look first into the blackness at a spot a foot away from your forehead. Now move your point of concentration to three feet away, and then six feet. Hold for a while until the point is firmly established. From there, turn the point 90º upward, on a line parallel to the body axis and reaching out above the head. Reach for the vibrations at that spot. When you find them, mentally pull them back into your head. (Monroe, *Journeys Out of Body*, p. 212.)

The idea here is to imagine a triangle of energy coming out of your eyes, converging at a point in front of you: You extend the point to the six foot mark, then swing it up over your head. This is when you will begin to feel "vibration." Bring the vibration down into your head by "reaching" for it. Next, Monroe suggests acclimatizing to the vibrational state by speeding it up. You turn it from a slightly uncomfortable buzz into a smoother sensation, or almost no sensation at all.

Finally, to get out-of-body (which we have not yet succeeded in doing this way), you are to get to the state of vibration, and practice reaching for objects with your "second body." You should reach for things as if, but not actually, stretching your arm toward it. Your eyes are closed, so it does not matter what you reach for. If you do this correctly, you will touch things that are physically out of your reach. You are even supposed to be able to reach through them to other things. To get all the way out-of-body, get in the vibrational state maintaining absolute control of your thought process. Imagine how nice it would be to float up and out of your body, and your "second body" should take the hint. To get back, you are simply to recall what it would be like to be lying on the bed again. You open your eyes only after you have gotten back inside.

This is an extreme condensation of Monroe's instructions, designed to give you an idea of his process. It is not a substitute for buying his book and following his lesson plan. He travels out-of-body. We do not.

Better yet, since Monroe admits that even his instructions are in some ways incomplete, contact the Institute and buy a set of tapes. They are designed to bring you well into the vibrational state without much work on your part. People have been reported to go out-of-body on their first exposure to Monroe's *Hemi-Sync* cassettes.

Chapter 13:
Get With The Program

This chapter is dedicated to a wide variety of types of dedication. If you take almost anything in nature, contemplate it, and dedicate yourself to it, you will experience a great high. If you have ever been in love, you will understand this phenomenon. Finding anything, even an insight, that rings absolutely true can resonate as ecstasy for quite a long while. If a person "finds Jesus," for example, the initial divine pleasure of "being saved" will be re-experienced every Sunday at church. At each new service, resonating frequencies are added to the initial striking of the bell, so that eventually, everything in life moves with divine ecstasy.

There are many devotional systems in the world today. Most of them would resent categorization of this sort, but this is what religion is, and why it works. There is nothing wrong with it. We have also included in this chapter the more modern sorts of programming, like est and fire walking. Again, these are peak experiences which produce highs that are later confirmed and expanded upon in subsequent seminars or workshops. All of these programs begin with a spark of truth — or at least one in the shape of truth — that ignites as a full flame in a human being. The particular dogma is fairly unimportant, as long as it does not call for you to hurt anyone. The downfall with almost all of these programs is that they invite addiction. Most practitioners of a faith or self-help organization will never shun your interest or dedication, no matter how obsessive it becomes.

It feels good to be in love with anything. It probably felt great to be in love with Nazism. Loving something, and devoting yourself to it, feels good. Don't let this feeling fool you into devoting yourself to something dangerous. You could get high by joining the mob and beating people up — but the toll on you and your victims hardly makes it worthwhile. Here are a few groups in which membership feels good, and the downsides are fairly minimal.

Est And The Seminar Phenomenon

Est was one of the first of the seminar programs. Originally, it consisted of a two-weekend "training," in which a leader with a microphone stood on a stage in front of a hundred or so people, and brought them to the realization that they were in control of the experience of life. The principle purpose of the est training was to change your experience of life, so that the situations you had been putting up with or trying to change, would clear up in the process of life itself. Despite the est clones and est-jargon, Werner Erhardt's concepts proved a valuable first lesson in how to use experience to move forward, rather than getting stuck. "Getting it" meant getting nothing and everything. It meant understanding that "getting it" is a state of mind. If you chose to be a person who "got it," you were. There were many useful concepts in the est training which, more than anything else, helped people realize that they were the only ones responsible for their experience of life.

The problem was that many est graduates experienced a high on leaving the original training, but then lost the effect. Their lives seemed to return to their original states. To combat this, est people created the Seminar Program, a relatively inexpensive way to "recharge" the est experience once a week. The seminar program still exists today, in one form or another.

But what happened to the est training? It was "retired," and re-placed with something called "The Forum," which itself has disap-peared. The ideas of est were new in the seventies, but already fairly integrated into American culture by the eighties. Most people who were going to take the training had, and those that had not, pretty well understood the principle of self as source.

Since est, many other similar training programs have been devel-oped and are still thriving. They can be valuable experiences. They can certainly get you high for several weeks, and then provide you with a community of like-minded people in which to regenerate your experience. The problems lie in these organizations' constant pressure on their members to find new trainees. Spreading the word becomes the word. In a devotional sense, this is fine. Sharing information is one of the only things worth doing with it. Still, if your main obstacle to being high is psychological or conceptual, the est-type seminars are a relatively painless catharsis, which can clear the way for you to move on to bigger and better things.

In the same basic category as est would be seminar programs like fire walking, Insights Seminars, or Robert Fritz's Institute for Human Evolution, and his program "Technologies for Creating." None of these are necessarily cults, but the majority do suffer from the problem — as do most churches — of having their greatest followers be the most needy people. It seems the strong move on and out, while the weaker stay behind and move up within the organization. The best way to find the right program for you is to talk to friends who have completed one of these seminars. There is really nothing in any of them that should screw you up too badly, although they all cost in the hundreds of dollars to try. Still, nearly all of the seminars make you feel really good for while, and provide you with some lasting tools to make your life work for you, rather than against you. Just keep in mind that the attachments you lose can just as easily be replaced by the programs that alleviated them.

A Course In Miracles

This started as a book, but has developed into a network of study groups throughout the world. *A Course in Miracles* was channeled by a group of psychologists. It is a profoundly rich assessment of the human condition and the path to awakening. To do the program, all you really need to do is buy the book and follow the instructions. There are many teachers — some qualified and some not so qualified — who work with the books to help others through the course. You can do it this way, but you do not have to. The book is designed for anyone to use.

It should take at least a year to get through the entire course, and then you will probably want to start over, or continue with your favorite exercises. Ultimately, the Course in Miracles takes the rest of your life, but throughout, you will gain a great number of insights into the practical ramifications of karma, spirituality and levels of awareness. The Course in Miracles provides you with direct experience of why you are here, where you came from, where you are going, and what to do about it. Truly understanding all this necessitates an alteration of consciousness.

The Course in Miracles is a milestone in the consciousness movement; everyone interested in higher consciousness should at least check out these books.

Right Action

Most of the major religions were developed to preserve the teachings of awakened people. Buddhism, for example, did not arise until after Buddha's death, when his followers decided to record what happened. Similarly, while Christ was alive, there was no need for Christianity; the awakened teacher was thought to be walking among us, and all we needed to do was follow him.

With or without an awakened teacher, you still have the ability to experience the bliss of his or her presence. As explained in the chapter on meditation, one way to experience bliss is to contemplate a person or deity to whom you are devoted. If you see this being as perfect, your love will grow. You will eventually see the object of your devotion manifest in everything around you. The world becomes a manifestation of the Buddha, the Christ, Kali, Krishna, or the guru of your choice. This can also be done with an idea. For example, you may realize one day that everything is light. "There is nothing else but light. Everything that seems to be something other than light is actually light, but appears to be something different because I cannot yet see it as light." Slowly, this awareness permeates your consciousness, and you are in a long-lasting, subtly altered state.

The best way to experience a devotional high is through action. You yourself become a manifestation of the deity or idea through your actions. For example, many devout Christians end up working in missions in the worst parts of their home town. A manifestation of the perfection of Christ is for his followers to put his compassion into practice.

Handing out food at a shelter for homeless people is a deeply rewarding experience — and not just because it relieves you of your feelings of guilt for being in a better socioeconomic position yourself. The process itself is a manifestation of a type of compassion. You are acknowledging one of your deepest needs: to help others. This can take a variety of forms — working in a hospital, an orphanage, an old-age home — but the high is the same in all of these cases. It comes from sharing.

Many people choose to share in less immediately tangible ways. Jehovah's Witnesses and Mormons, for example, go door-to-door sharing their gospel. Other people use their time off to teach illiterate people how to read and write. Even professional healing — like Mariel and Reichian — are practices of a devotional discipline. In any of these cases, the giver is a person who believes strongly in the value of what they have to offer. Watching someone else benefit confirms this value, and feels good.

It sounds too simple to get high by doing nice things for people, but it works — especially if you feel you are manifesting some kind of

140

truth. Your actions become an extension of something much bigger than yourself. You are only a conduit for a greater energy, which, as it flows through you on its way to help others, gets you remarkably high.

Chapter Fourteen: Less Is More: Getting High By Doing Without

Many religions advocate deprivation. Monks of most faiths are told at one time or another to fast, take vows of silence, cut themselves off from the world, practice celibacy, or even wear patches over their eyes. These techniques are employed as teaching tools. A monk who does not talk for a year may learn, for example, how he has always used speech in order to feed his ego rather than to help others. A monk who takes a vow of celibacy may gain an understanding that, for him, sex has been wasting vital life energy. By fasting, one might learn discipline, and be better prepared for the perils of the spiritual journey he hopes to take. (Some monks practiced fasting so that they would be able to meditate for weeks at a time without worrying about food.)

Our interest in deprivation has nothing to do with such goals. While exploiting some of the techniques developed over the ages, the deprivations outlined here are listed for the exclusive purpose of providing you access to altered states of consciousness. Do not fool yourself that you are fasting for better health, or depriving yourself of speech to make up for lies you have told. Keep your head out of this.

Deprivation forces your mind to rebalance. States of consciousness are dependent on our perceptions of reality. They can even be defined as such. By altering the manner in which we perceive reality, we alter the state of consciousness. In the techniques of deprivation, we alter the total picture of reality by removing a piece or two. A world with no news reports or media is extremely different from one with a radio blasting the headlines twenty-four hours a day. We have gotten very used to the stimuli that surround us — so much so, that we have become deadened. Depriving ourselves of just one of the elements of the perceptual landscape to which we have become accustomed will necessitate a reactivation of our learning centers. Deprived of sight, we will have to learn how to "hear" walls. With the mind busy testing the new environment, the consciousness is free to roam around and play.

Deprivations are not penance. They are temporary closures, which allow other things to open. Often, we shut our eyes in order to think more clearly. With unwanted stimuli removed, the mind no longer needs to act like a filtering system. More brain "RAM" can be put to work on the real problem at hand.

One of the principal problems on the path to spiritual awakening is called the "peripheral" attack. This takes the form of distractions. The only reason distractions take hold is because the person views himself as somehow separate from that which is around him. To the enlightened individual, the self and the world are the same. He experiences a great unity of consciousness. This is the "oneness" spoken about in spiritual texts. As we are not awakened people, we need to eliminate the possibility of distractions so that we do not blame our problems on things that seem to be out of our control. For example, if when you meditate, you find you are consistently distracted by mosquitoes flying around you, you have two choices. The harder choice is to learn to become invisible. Then the bugs will not know you are there, and you will not get bitten. The easier choice is to meditate in a place with no bugs.

Deprivations do not "deprive" us — they free us. They remove external influences so that we can experience our inner states more subtly. A common misconception about the Jewish holiday Yom Kippur is that the day's fast is some sort of penance. It is not. The Jews fast on their day of atonement so that they can more fully concentrate on their prayers. Similarly, by experiencing any deprivation, we free ourselves to concentrate on what we want to.

In any period of deprivation, you will experience moments of great stress. If you have been blindfolded for two days, for example, you may suddenly get the unbearable urge to look around. It is precisely at these moments, however, when the potential for great alterations of consciousness are possible. With each threshold of "discomfort" comes an opportunity for greater clarity. Still, you must use care and judgment. Most deprivations work best under supervision. Find a friend who knows you well, and whose orders you promise to follow. When your friend says you have had enough, quit whatever deprivation you are trying.

The easiest deprivations are the ones that take the shortest amount of time and do not involve any vital bodily functions such as eating or sleeping. But as with any of the following techniques, it is important that you take ample time to prepare and then even more time to recover. You do not want to go to work the morning after a week of sleeplessness.

Flotation Tanks

Developed by John Lilly and later made famous in the film *Altered States*, flotation tanks are the easiest way to explore deprivation as a method of getting high. Flotation tanks are dark boxes filled with very salty water. You go inside, shut the lid, and float on your back (the salt allows you to do this effortlessly) in total darkness and silence. Except for the feeling of warm water against your head and back, you receive no neural stimuli.

The theory here is that with no external influences, you are free to experience your internal state. You begin to hear the tones that resonate within your head all the time, but are usually drowned out by other noises. In the blackness, your optic nerves are free to discharge stored energy in the form of hallucinations. Your body is free to experience the sensations that it generates by itself, freed of gravity and muscular effort.

It may take a little while to get used to the sensation of being in a tank. The water level tends to end up near your ears, and it might be uncomfortable for you to let water inside them. If you think this will be the case, bring comfortable earplugs. This will also eliminate the influence of the sound of the water moving around in your ears if you bob up and down. We also recommend eating lightly or not at all before floating. You do not want to spend your entire session listening to your food digest, or feeling it move through the alimentary canal.

Most reasonably sized towns have places that rent flotation tanks on an hourly basis. Check New Age publications or ask at New Age bookshops. If there is nowhere to float near you, and you have your heart set on this method, you can buy plans for a tank, a tank kit, or even a fully assembled tank for use in your own home. You can purchase one through the Samadhi Tank Company, 2123 Lake Shore Drive, Los Angeles, CA 90039. We would not recommend purchasing one until you are sure you want to invest a lot of time into this path. The last thing you need is an unused float tank in your garage.

The best source of information about floating is Michael Hutchison's *The Book of Floating: Exploring the Private Sea*. But the most daring explorer of tanks and the associated states of consciousness is still John Lilly, who documents his work most successfully in *The Deep Self* (NY: Warner Books, 1977). This book even has plans for tanks in its appendix, as well as valuable experiments to try during tank sessions. But be forewarned: Lilly usually ingested chemicals before going into the tank. His experiences are a combination of sensory deprivation and ketamine experimentation. Still, much of what Lilly experienced in the tank is available to us without taking drugs. A journey inward with drugs may be a little more obvious and a little faster, but the reality is not the same. If you are journeying within to see what's inside, then do that. If you take drugs before going into the tank, you are not looking at yourself but at your drugged self. There is a big difference. The point of deprivation is to remove influences, not to introduce them. Go into the tank with as little as possible and your mind will expand naturally and effortlessly. What you will see is what is really there.

At first, most people experience only a great relaxation. (This can take a while, as most people first become acutely aware of their own body sounds and phosphene discharge.) Then, thoughts about other things slowly enter your consciousness. When this happens, remind yourself that you are inside a tank and there is nothing but you. The problems of your day may move into your consciousness, but you must realize that they are not acting upon you in the tank. Anything you are not experiencing at this moment is not real. It is memory. It is a story. Your presence in the tank is the only reality. External influences can only affect you by your own choice. In the tank, it does not matter who is president or to whom you are married. You have the opportunity to be free of everything from light and sound to your job and your financial status. The only thing left is your consciousness.

It is very difficult to shut off the internal chatter of thoughts. We usually live under such stress that it is difficult to do anything in a tank except release thought. This incessant internal monologue may never fade away. Do not try to suppress it. Let it rattle on as long as it wants to. Just slowly stop paying attention. Whenever you realize you are involved in an internal monologue, just say to yourself "blah blah blah." Acknowledge that your mind needs to talk, and let it. Your real consciousness, however, need not be involved.

Imagine, for example, that your mind and your consciousness are both in the same huge room. See your mind as a little radio in the corner somewhere that was left on. (Worse yet, it wasn't even left on music, but on an AM talk radio station.) There is no way to turn the radio off, so just leave it alone. Look around other parts of the room. Find doors, push through walls, or whatever you want. Do not worry about it. Listen if you like, but when you get bored, simply float away. You can catch up with what your mind is saying when you get back, the same way that you can understand a soap opera even after a month of not watching.

Eventually — it may not be your first or even your fifth float session when this happens — you will move out of the mind's jurisdiction. You will experience the infinite possibilities of a world with no sights, sounds, or sensations. You will have the experience of being asleep while fully conscious. You may even begin to travel out-of-body, or out of the time-space continuum.

Space has nothing to do with area, distance or volume. There is just as much space within you as outside of you. And for inward journeys, you don't need to involve NASA or huge cash reserves. Lilly has described dozens of levels of consciousness he has reached on his journeys inward, and labeled them by number. On each of the different levels, there appear to be different personalities one can meet. These, supposedly, are "aliens" of a different sort: conscious beings who live interdimensionally rather than "out there" somewhere. We will surely document our interactions with these beings (whether they turn out to be real or imaginary) long before we develop the technology to reach out into outer space to find other inhabited planets at our own level of reality.

But getting high in an isolation tank is a much easier proposition than developing a relationship with an interdimensional being. All you need to do is learn how to move past the emissions of your normally overworked senses. Once you learn to shorten the initial period of disorientation and sensory discharge, you will move into a deeply relaxed yet extremely clear state of awareness.

Temporary Blindness

Another fairly fast-acting form of sensory deprivation is blindfolding. Much like an extended form of pin-the-tail-on-the-donkey, this technique challenges our ability to function without one of our chief orientation systems: sight. Give yourself at least two days to try this. One of the most elucidating moments of all is waking up on the second day and remembering that you cannot see.

To do this deprivation properly, you need to buy eyepatches or a sleeping shade that completely blocks out light. You should not have to close your eyes, and you should not have to worry about something falling off if you move the wrong way. Your temporary blindness must be effortless. Most drugstores have eyepatches with adhesive edges that are used for recovering eye surgery patients. Do not just buy the black pirate patches, they are made for aesthetic purposes, and not to block out light.

You can try fashioning your own eye patches which may prove more comfortable than what are available in stores. Here is one solution: Get cloth and something completely opaque, like aluminum foil. Sew two pieces of cloth together with the aluminum foil sandwiched inbetween. Make two patches of this sort in whatever shapes best fit your face. You want the patch to attach to your forehead, cheek, nose and temple. To affix the patches to your face, use the most comfortable porous tape available. Using something like adhesive tape will not harm you, but it will be more uncomfortable and you will be forced to associate your blindness with a negative physical sensation.

Once you have bought or made your eyepatches, you need to prepare your home. Get everything sharp, delicate, or precariously perched well out of reach. Check the floor for anything you might trip over. Prepare a lot of food so that you do not need to cook anything. Line up everything from toilet paper and towels to socks and underwear. While it works best to have a friend with whom to do things, there may also be times when you are alone, and you will have a better time if you know your safety has been assured. Wear shoes of some sort all the time. Do not smoke or use any kind of flame.

It is also a good idea to set up a "darkroom." If the tape around your patches gets loose or uncomfortable, you should be able to retreat into a closet where you can make necessary repairs. While the closet may not be pitch black, if you keep your eyes closed it should stay dark enough to prevent any light from entering your eyes through the lids.

As long as you have a companion with you, you can do anything you like. Go for walks in the city and in nature. Take a subway ride or a rollercoaster ride. Have sex, talk about philosophy, play music — do anything you like.

The first thing most people notice is how hard it is to get around without sight. You may begin to feel great compassion for those who are blind. This is fine. Just don't let your guilt consume you. It may seem to you like you are playing around with something very serious to someone else. Let these kinds of feelings surface and then fade away. Next, after most of the first day has passed, you will begin to notice that your other senses begin to improve. Your sense of touch may seem extraordinarily clear. You will begin to "hear" how a room's resonance changes when you get near a wall. Your perception of space will change.

You may also find that you experience two kinds of blindness. In one mode, you look into the blackness before you. You observe the shapes and random phosphene discharge. You are staring into blackness. When you are not thinking about this blackness, you are in a different sort of blindness. It is as if sight simply does not exist. This may not happen until the second day, but when it does, you will begin to understand the point of this deprivation.

When you are finished (try to take at least a whole weekend for this experience), reintroduce yourself to sight very slowly. Get into a very dark room and remove your patches without opening your eyes. Get used to the light that penetrates your eyelids. Then, very slowly, open your eyes in the dark room. You will probably be able to see almost everything. Slowly reintroduce yourself to light, preferably from natural sources. Some people experience a dryness of the eyes at first. Have some optical saline drops, or a product called "Tears II" around just in case you need some extra lubrication at first. As with all deprivations, be sure to consult your physician before trying anything.

No Sleep

This is a tricky one, because the amount of sleep deprivation that gets you high is pretty close to the amount that makes you go temporarily nuts. Depriving yourself of sleep means depriving yourself of dreams. The activity of your subconscious mind needs to find an outlet elsewhere. Laurie Anderson (a popular performance artist) is reported to go for days without sleep in order to produce a state of consciousness in which she can be extremely creative because she has more direct access to impulses and images which are usually reserved for dreamlife.

Sleep deprivation may be the closest technique in this book to psychedelics use for several reasons. First, after a day or so, your state of consciousness is extremely altered. Colors look more vivid. Three-dimensional objects look two-dimensional, and vice versa. Sight, in general, seems very improved. Sensitivity to light increases dramatically. Thoughts and images that resemble Jungian archetypes seem to come from everywhere. On the downside, and also like psychedelics, there are periods of time when the "trip" is irreversible. After a couple of days of no sleep, you cannot just tell your body to fall asleep. Your sleep clock still functions, albeit erratically. Just because you decide you have had enough does not mean you can go to sleep right away. It may take six hours before a window of sleep opportunity presents itself. You may also feel extremely tired for the next few days. You need a good, long recovery period. Like a drug, sleeplessness must be allowed to run its course.

To prepare for an extended period of sleep deprivation, you need to isolate yourself from the people who depend on you. You will be in no condition to make .decisions for yourself or anyone else. You should not deal with phone calls, employers, family or salespeople at the door.

Pick yourself a supervisor, if possible, who will monitor your behavior and tell you when you have had enough. This person can also serve as your cook and maid. After two or three days of sleeplessness, you may turn into a slob. If you plan to do this alone, prepare as much food as you can ahead of time. Also, set up rows of trash cans lined with plastic bags. Eat on paper plates and just throw things out when you are done. Do not cook with fire. You will be very forgetful and may burn your house down. Just put things in a micro-wave or eat them cold. Be sure to eat well. Take vitamins and/or amino acids during your sleeplessness as well as for several days before and afterwards. Drink plenty of fluids, stay warm, do yoga or other simple exercises, change your clothes and shower daily.

It is very easy to get cranky when you have had no sleep. But if you recognize that this is happening, it should not be too difficult to deal with. Crankiness looks worse than it feels. The worst part of it is that we know how we must look, and feel bad for being mean. Establish at the outset with anyone you are going to see during your sleeplessness that you will be in an extremely bitchy mood. Channeled crankiness is really a form of creativity. Roseanne Barr and Don Rickles made careers of this.

The easiest way to do this deprivation is at a meditation retreat. No one else has to know what you are doing, and you do not have to interact with anyone at all. Our friend David experienced his first extended sleeplessness at a writers' retreat. He stayed up for about three days writing, then lost the urge to sleep and stayed awake for several more days. Everyone knew he was acting a little trippy, but that is to be expected from writers in retreat. The best thing about it was that his meals were made for him and that there were people to do his laundry.

But once you stop worrying about what other people think about you, you are free to pass through to a state of profound clarity. Thoughts do not come very quickly, but they come in extremely vivid and well-articulated imagery. You begin to think in metaphors, visualizing your thoughts in new ways. Your creative and contemplative powers may be very enhanced, so have paper, pencils, art supplies, music instruments and a tape recorder around. Speaking your thoughts into a tape recorder may be the easiest way to preserve your insights.

While we do not advocate the use of drugs, the easiest way to end a period of sleeplessness is with calming herbs or an evening cognac. Try to hold out until sundown, so that your sleep clock has a fighting chance of getting back on schedule. Take it easy for the next two days, as you slowly reintegrate into the real world.

No Talking

Try not to speak for a week. Create a situation where this is feasible, like at a retreat or even a motel in some beautiful place. Bring a paper and pencil with you, and write a note telling the proprietor you cannot speak. Then do whatever you want without talking to anyone.

In the strictest sense, a vow of silence is not really a deprivation. You still receive everything you normally do. The only thing you lose is the ability to express yourself and your intentions. But by depriving yourself of something as simple as speech, you take the first step to removing effort from your life.

After even one day, a feeling of extreme satisfaction will come over you. Unable to manipulate other people, you will lose the urge to control things. Concepts like needs and self disappear. You may begin to smile for no reason.

No News Is Good News

Another simple yet profound deprivation is a media blackout. Do whatever you have to do to stay ignorant of world events. Avoid stories of all kinds. The only things you should talk about or listen to must involve your immediate experience. Nothing else matters or exists.

This is more difficult than it sounds. You must avoid television, radio, newspapers, magazines, and the printed word of almost any kind other than maps or directions for something. Harder still is to avoid talking about things other than the present moment. It is nearly impossible to go to work without hearing somebody talk about a famous trial or plane crash. You cannot hear this kind of information. It is even more difficult to keep yourself from getting involved in conversations about stories. Even telling a stranger what you do for a living is a story. Your profession, unless you are engaged in it at the precise moment, has nothing to do with your interaction with a stranger you meet in the park. The rules in this deprivation are demanding but clear cut. Do not speak about or listen to anything other than what's germane to the moment.

The longer you can keep this up, the better. Enough time needs to pass so that it really feels like the world has kept spinning without your knowledge. Governments may have changed hands, the president may have sent troops to Burma, and nuclear fusion may have led to the discovery of God. Unless it happens in your field of vision, it is immaterial. Out of sight, out of mind is your way of life.

Remarkable changes in your attitude towards life take place in just a few days. Some people experience an alteration in consciousness after just six hours of not consulting their answering machines. A commodities trader would probably find this deprivation exercise impossible. But even for those of us who are not compulsively tied to stories, disconnection from the global drama is a remarkably freeing experience. Dropping out, so to speak, opens a whole new world of directly experiential living.

One of the easiest ways to partake of a media deprivation is to travel cross country. Hop in the car with some cash, a credit card and a pretty partner (if you can find one) and just go. The difference between this and a normal vacation is that you are not just vacationing from a place or a job, but from everything. All that is left is the process by which you experience life. Nothing you have ever done or plan to do matters. You become nothing but your experience. After a day or so of catharsis (similar to the discharges of sound and light you experience in a floatation tank) you will begin to feel the freedom that media deprivation affords.

It will not be boring. On the contrary, your senses will become so heightened that everything will seem as though you are experiencing it for the first time. Instead of looking at things, classifying them and moving on, you will begin to look just for looking's sake. There is no reason to remember anything, because there is no reason to repeat anything. You simply move through time and space with no memories, no cares, and no stakes. This is the ultimate vacation.

Like the aftermath of any intense high, you will need to reintegrate into normal life slowly. Many of the things you have been holding on to for security may seem useless when you get back. Even your job may seem pointless. Don't take any rash actions at first, until you have had time to get back in to the motion of the regular world, if you choose to rejoin it.

Fasting

Fasting is more of a physical trip than anything else, but we include it here because it is certainly the most obvious of the deprivations to try. We did not get high from not eating, just got hungry. Still, for centuries people have been using fasting as a purification, so there is probably something to it.

The most beneficial aspect of fasting is that it frees your body of the process of digestion, and frees your mind from the concern about food. You streamline your day, release the toxins in your body, increase the sensitivity of your alimentary canal and clarify your spiritual intentions. Your day is streamlined because ingesting and digesting food is no longer one of your concerns. Your time is no longer spent between and during meals. The day divides itself by your thoughts or activities instead. For those of you who have a fixation with eating, this is a major change of focus. Also, by clearing your insides of food, you free up many organs of your body, not to mention your bloodstream. The digestive tract is the seat of human emotion. Most stomach aches have major psychological components. By taking food out of your system, you increase your sensitivity to the physical manifestations of your emotional states. People eat when they are upset because it quite literally numbs their insides. The stomach and intestines are given food, a new problem to deal with, so that they no longer embody your emotional life so tangibly. But without food, the alimentary canal becomes more unified with your consciousness. No longer relegated to crushing and sorting out matter, these organs can listen to signals from you instead of your food. Similarly, you are in a much better position to hear what your body is telling you when you have not just shoved a Snickers bar inside.

One of the later effects of a fast is on your ego. Eating is a taking. To eat is to sacrifice another life — however simple — in order to energize your own. There is nothing wrong in this. We have to eat to keep our consciousness functioning. But to deprive ourselves of food momentarily allows us to re-evaluate our position in the scheme of things. We can step out, temporarily, of the food chain and the fight for survival. Fasting, we can experience what it is like to take nothing. Life is defined by the ability and effort to maintain itself. If you do not eat, you exercise conscious will over the very animal instinct that created us out of the primordial sludge. There is a simple, egoless state of consciousness associated with this realization that is the "high" of fasting.

In order to fast, you must do it correctly. Don't just stop eating. Your doctor will know the best kind of fast for you. The general rules are to begin slowly and end slowly. Don't have a huge meal just before you fast. This defeats the purpose. One fast that works well is to eat only brown rice for a day or so to clear out your system. When you do fast, drink plenty of fluid and do exercise. If you allow yourself to drink juices rather than just water, you will feel a lot better and be able to go a lot longer. When you break the fast, be sure to do it gradually. Don't fast for four days and then eat a steak dinner. Start on some fruit or melon, then work up to simple vegetable carbohydrates. Be sure to get a check-up before you undertake anything like this. Any decent holistic doctor can give you instructions for fasting that suit your particular metabolism.

Chapter Fifteen:
Staying High

Human beings tend to experience life through contrasts. We know we are experiencing love if we feel sadness after our loved one is gone. We know we are happy only when we have been relieved of sadness. Similarly, to get "high" presupposes there is such a thing as low. This is an unfortunately limited view of the world — one that depends on duality and unworthiness in order to perpetuate itself.

Race drivers say they love the danger of their sport because it makes them appreciate life more. Knowing they might die tomorrow makes them value the present. In the same way, many of us measure the quality of our lives by the quantity of peak experiences we can accumulate. This assumes that somehow regular life is inadequate. It is not.

It is possible to be high most or all the time. This does not mean being disoriented or stoned. It means being extraordinarily alert and aware. As we discussed in the introduction, the mind acts like a filter for our awareness. As we feel safe and more a part of whatever life may bring to us, the less we need that filter — the less we need to resist the natural flow of being. This flow is pure movement and pure bliss.

A "rush" is a momentary experience of the movement of the cosmos. Everything is actually moving all the time, but we have shut off our awareness of it. When we get momentarily high, disoriented, or free, we experience movement. Consciousness itself is merely a movement receptor. The more movement one's consciousness opens to, the more alive it becomes. When one's consciousness becomes totally alive — that is, aware of all the movements that there are — it is fully awakened. The illusions and attachments we cling to prevent us from experiencing true movement. We create a fiction called "reality" in order to limit our sense of the universe's movement. Altered states of consciousness detach us momentarily from this fictional reality and allow us to see it as illusion, or at least as arbitrary.

From the time we realize we are conscious beings, we are trying to wake up. Children spin in circles on their mothers' kitchen floors to stimulate their consciousness with movement. People get high on drugs as an attempt to experience movement in their lives. It is not that there is a particular state of consciousness everyone gropes towards. The *alteration* of consciousness is what feels so good. The changes from one state to another are what imitate birth, death, and even enlightenment.

But getting high is only an imitation of something even more real. It is like a flight simulator. The Tibetans performed their *Book of the Dead* rituals as a test run for death and rebirth. Most of us who are concerned with things like reincarnation, out-of-body travel and past-life regression are actually preoccupied with surviving our own deaths. Likewise, getting high imitates the kind of change that may occur at death. By getting high and returning to the straight world, we suggest to ourselves that we can beat death, or at least practice the process of dying.

To be high all the time would be to eliminate from your consciousness the dualities of high and straight, good and bad, mind and body, and life and death. You would no longer experience alterations of consciousness. All that would be left is the experience of movement. It would not be disorienting, because you would see how you, yourself, are part of this movement. You are not passively carried by the flow of movement but neither are you expending energy to keep up with it. You simply realize how you are the flow. The rest is a free ride.

YOU WILL ALSO WANT TO READ:

☐ **85182 PSYCHEDELIC SHAMANISM, The Cultivation, Preparation and Shamanic Use of Psychotropic Plants,** *by Jim DeKorne.* From the author of *The Hydroponic Hot House* comes the boldest exploration of psychedelic plants since Terence McKenna's *Food of the Gods.* DeKorne is a "psychonaut" exploring the "imaginal realms" through personal experimentation and scholarly research. He guides the reader through the history and lore of psychotropic plants, with advice on how to handle the eerie "Entities" one encounters in "hyperspace." Plants and combinations covered include: Belladonna, Alkaloids, D-Lysergic Acid Amide, Mescaline, Ayahuasca, Psilocybin, and more. *1994, 8½ x 11, 163 pp, Illustrated, soft cover.* $19.95.

☐ **91085 SECRETS OF A SUPER HACKER,** *by The Knightmare, with the Introduction by Gareth Branwyn.* The most amazing book on computer hacking ever written! Step-by-step illustrated details on the techniques used by hackers to get your data. The how-to text is highlighted with bare-knuckle tales of the Knightmare's hacks. No person concerned with computer security should miss this amazing manual of mayhem. *1994, 8½ x 11, 205 pp, Illustrated, soft cover.* $19.95.

☐ **61139 METHODS OF DISGUISE, Revised and Expanded 2nd Edition,** *by John Sample.* Here is an incredible, completely illustrated book on how to disguise yourself! Covers everything from "quick-change" methods to long-term, permanent disguises. Learn to disguise yourself so completely even old friends won't recognize you. Over 130 detailed drawings. *1993, 5½ x 8½, 264 pp, Illustrated, soft cover.* $14.95.

☐ **14099 THE ART & SCIENCE OF DUMPSTER DIVING,** *by John Hoffman.* This book will show you how to get just about anything you want or need — food, clothing, furniture, building materials, entertainment, luxury goods, tools, toys — you name it — ABSOLUTELY FREE! Take a guided tour of America's back alleys where amazing wealth is carelessly discarded. Hoffman will show you where to find the good stuff, how to rescue it and how to use it. *1993, 8½ x 11, 152 pp, Illustrated, soft cover.* $12.95.

Loompanics Unlimited
PO Box 1197
Port Townsend, WA 98368

SF95

Please send me the books I have checked above. I have enclosed $_____ which includes $4.00 for shipping and handling of 1 to 3 books, $6.00 for 4 or more. Washington residents include 7.9% sales tax.

Name_____

Address _____

City/State/Zip _____

Now accepting VISA and MasterCard.
To place credit card orders *only,* call 1-800-380-2230,
9am to 4pm, PST, Monday thru Friday.